CONNECTION MODE

"Nancy Green is a true visionary with a huge heart. *Connection Mode* is her gift to all of us, an insightful and inspirational book that educates and empowers the reader.

In the most positive way, *Connection Mode* rouses those who may think that a diagnosis—autism, PTSD, ADHD, OCD, anxiety disorder, and any other mental health condition—limits who they are and what they can do. With humor and heart, *Connection Mode* goes beyond encouraging others to believe they have the power to change their brain and nervous system. This unique book hands readers an exclusive, powerful, and effortlessly understood road map that truly makes it possible for anyone to experience an easier life.

Engaging, entertaining, and educational, *Connection Mode* is a long-awaited resource that I will be recommending to all my patients and family members! I would venture to say that Nancy has revealed and defined a most important step that can and will bring us all closer to peace in both our inner and outer world."

—**Melinda Roland**, PT, CST-D

"*Connection Mode* is a fantastic book! It pulls back the curtain, revealing how we may not realize we never finished our lower brain development, that our nervous system isn't working as intended, and how those variables can greatly affect our lives in a myriad of ways. As a parent, I can testify to how this creative approach helped my child with his behavior and self-esteem when all other methods were falling short. As a physician, I can highly recommend that patients empower themselves with the wealth of knowledge and solutions offered in *Connection Mode* to make a lifetime investment in their health and happiness.

If you are searching for more harmony in your home, a greater sense of well-being, and sound health of your body and mind, read this riveting book, and discover how to live your life in connection mode."

—**Andrea Lorenze**, MD

"Nancy's ability to understand the complexities of the brain and nervous system and teach them to children, parents, and educators with such ease, understanding, and humor is not only inspiring but also life changing for everyone. *Connection Mode* is for anyone who is curious about living their best life, as well as anyone who wants to help others achieve their best life and experience profound changes.

As an elementary school counselor, I now understand children on a deeper level and help them, too, live their life in connection mode. For teachers, *Connection Mode* also offers hope, specific ways to connect with students, and simple actions to make it easy for everyone to learn—all why teachers I know have become so excited by this approach. On a personal level, I can't even imagine what our family's life would have been like in 2020 if we hadn't already been integrating the approaches presented in *Connection Mode*. If you work with children or you're a parent—or you just want to live your best life—this book is a must-read!"

—**Jen Larson,** MSEd, school counselor

"The Brain Highways approach presented in *Connection Mode* is one of the best. I can attest from personal experience with my family and patients to how effective this approach is. Filled with true stories that illuminate how to interact with those who may be in protection mode, easy-to-understand examples of how any of us can get stuck in protection mode, and so many of the very best techniques offered in the Brain Highways program, this revealing and insightful book will benefit all adults and kids."

—**Robert Schwartz,** MD, FAAPMR

"I have personally observed the life-changing results of Nancy's work with children and adults with PTSD and cognitive and emotional processing challenges. *Connection Mode's* innovative approach is both time-tested and the real deal. While I work primarily with veterans and their families, I highly recommend this compelling, user-friendly manual for everyone with a nervous system."

—**Judy Weaver,** founder of Connected Warriors

Nancy Sokol Green

CONNECTION
MODE

How to Change Your Brain for an Easier Life

RIVER GROVE
BOOKS

Published by River Grove Books
Austin, TX
www.rivergrovebooks.com

Distributed by River Grove Books

Design and composition by Greenleaf Book Group
Cover design by Greenleaf Book Group
Cover image: ©iStockphoto/mbbirdy

Publisher's Cataloging-in-Publication data is available.

Print ISBN: 978-1-63299-607-7

eBook ISBN: 978-1-63299-608-4

First Edition

For Jim, finally

CONTENTS

INTRODUCTION

I t is back in the '80s, and my husband wants to teach me how to drive a Volkswagen with a stick shift. I'm sitting in the driver's seat, waiting for my first lesson.

Yet my husband (the guy with the master's in scientific instrumentation) begins with this long, technical explanation about the machinations of the clutch. In truth, I tune him out as soon as he starts talking about some pressure plate and a throw-out bearing. All I want to know is: How do I put the car in reverse to back out of the driveway?

And it is that same mindset—make it simple, just tell me what I need to know to make my life easier *right now*—that motivated me to write this book. There are also my twenty years of guiding thousands of adults and kids in a program I created called Brain Highways. In these courses, participants have lots of fun as they discover and unleash an amazing power inherent to all of us: We can change our nervous system and brain so that our life is surprisingly easier than what we now experience. Of course, what "easier" specifically means for each person will vary. That's because we struggle in different ways.

But, in general, an easier life means that our brain and nervous system do not escalate from 1 to 100 when we are upset. We no longer find it challenging to focus. We experience amiable, thoughtful relationships. That relentless, inexplicable, never-ending anxiety has stopped looming over us. We find learning to be joyful. Best of all, we no longer wake up with that same dread and despair that today's struggles will be no different from those of every other day. That's what happens once we automate parts of our brain and nervous system so that we're now wired to respond in different ways. It's this new and efficient circuitry that makes an easier life a reality.

Not surprisingly, the adults and kids going through the Brain Highways program also want to cut right to the chase. Their thinking is straightforward: Skip the technical terms. Tell me the answers to questions like: How does my nervous system play such a whopping role when I argue or shut down in relationships? How does my brain literally change (and not in a good way) if its primitive parts keep leading my life? What is my lower brain, and why should I care if I never finished developing it? And then, please show me how to get out of the driveway and on to an easier life. Since I want you to have that information as well, this book guides you down the path toward an easier life. The book is divided into three parts: "Our Nervous System: Features, Nuances, and Hiccups," "The Lower Brain Connection: An Unexpected Possibility," and "The Nervous System's Trifecta: Getting Started Right Now." While it might sound odd, these specific sections were somewhat inspired from a scene in *The Wizard of Oz*.

This scene happens after the wizard has been debunked as a complete fraud, but Dorothy and her friends still do not know how she is going to get home. And then Glinda, the Good Witch, appears out of the sky and lands right in front them. She tells Dorothy that she only needs to click her heels together, and—voilà!—Dorothy will be back home. Oh, and guess what? Glinda drops a little bombshell when she shares that Dorothy has had this power all along.

Well, that's when the Scarecrow (who clearly has acquired a brain along the way) interjects with a legitimate question. He asks Glinda, "Then why didn't you tell her before?" To which Glinda responds, "Because she wouldn't have believed me."

So the first part of this book gives you a chance to believe that your nervous system and brain *are* front and center in everything that you do. Equally important is that you believe you already have this incredible power to change your brain and nervous system. We really do have this extraordinary gift.

But what if Glinda had shared only that Dorothy always had the power to go home and left it up to her to figure out what that meant? That would have been incredibly frustrating, if not downright mean. So, to make sure that you are not left dangling, I included the second and third parts of this book.

However, to explain the reason for the second part, I need to insert a scene that never appeared in the original film. In this new scene, Dorothy discovers something about her ruby slippers. Only a few measly stitches have been keeping each sole in place! But here is the big gotcha. Until those soles are secured to the rest of each shoe, the shoes will not work as intended. That means that until then, Dorothy is going to experience never-ending frustration and stress every time she clicks her heels together, only to realize that she is still standing in the very same place. To get out of Oz and on with her life, Dorothy cannot gloss over the part where she also needs to secure those soles.

In a similar way, people who have already tried many approaches that yielded little or no lasting changes may discover that they did not finish their lower brain development during their first year of life. Thankfully, the brain allows for a plan B, meaning that they can complete that development at any time. However, until those highways are in place, their brain will not work as intended. They will feel as stuck as Dorothy (if she never addresses those soles), even if they now diligently try to change their nervous system. That's because finishing the lower brain development is a *huge*, integral part of repairing our nervous system's landscape. For many people, the information in the second part of the book is the missing piece of the puzzle.

Once you arrive at the third part, you will now be ready to learn specific, pragmatic ways to address each component of the nervous system's trifecta. Learning how to resolve, repair, and replenish your nervous system—all on your own—is what puts you on the path to an easier life.

To be clear, I am not a doctor, scientist, or any kind of therapist. I am an educator. I have always been someone who loves to teach, with a passion and penchant for simplifying important but complex information. While I often present other people's research in ways that are livelier than most expect, I do so for only one reason. Opening new doors may then make it possible for more people, especially kids, to also benefit from these brilliant researchers' discoveries.

For this book, I've drawn from many neuroscientists' conclusions, including the groundbreaking work of Stephen W. Porges. However, at first glance, these notable researchers' influence may not appear obvious on these pages. For starters, I opted not to use any of the traditional, multisyllable words to describe the nervous system's anatomy and physiology.

Instead (staying true to those who want to cut right to the chase), I have boldly reduced the explanation of the entire nervous system to one simple statement: We are either in protection mode or connection mode. I do admit that is a sparse description of an intricate, multifaceted part of our biology. But it's also an easy way to quickly understand how our nervous system works.

For example, we shift into protection mode as soon as our nervous system assesses a potential threat. Once that happens, we are now operating from the primitive, survival parts of our brain. Yet, by focusing on the word *protection*—rather than the word *survival*—we are reminded of something important. We are now behaving in a way that our nervous system thinks *will truly protect us*.

On the other hand, we are in connection mode whenever our nervous system does not perceive any danger. Here, we are operating from another part of our nervous system. Yet the term *connection mode* also reminds us of something important. Yes, we are instinctively programmed to survive. But we are equally wired to connect with others. That, too, is embedded in our neurobiology. Most importantly, once we understand how our behavior in protection mode differs greatly from how we act in connection mode, it's easy to make this conclusion: If we want an easier life, we need to spend far more time in connection mode than protection mode.

Throughout the book, I also take other liberties to explain how the brain and nervous system specifically work. For example, I sometimes imagine what our brain and nervous system would say if they could talk. So this is not a book for those who are looking for statistical references and cited peer-reviewed research. But it is a book for those who are curious about how their brain and nervous system may be unknowingly sabotaging their lives and want to know what they can do about that right now.

I also do not believe that serious subjects, such as the brain and nervous system, always mean that we need to *be serious* when learning about them. Fortunately, that thought is right in line with how the brain likes to learn. It turns out that the brain loves being playful, and it processes information much more easily whenever we are relaxed. That's why this is more of an entertaining than scholarly book, infused with humor, analogies, and lots of amusing, intriguing, and tug-at-your-heart stories.

However, when choosing which stories would appear in this book, I always had one thought in mind. While these stories may be about me, family members, or Brain Highways participants, they are also *your* stories. That means it will be impossible for you not to "see" yourself, your family members, your work colleagues, or anyone else you know in whatever story has happened to one of us. When it comes to our nervous system and brain, we are far more alike than different. But these stories additionally reveal what kind of amazing changes can happen once we start living most of our life in connection mode. That, too, can be you.

Of course, nothing in this book should be considered medical or psychological advice or treatment. My only intent is to widen your view, so that you might ponder different reasons why you (or others) continue to struggle. And when we widen the view, it's only about addition, not subtraction. That means you do not need to quit whatever has already proven helpful to you if you now also decide to consider more ways to help your brain and nervous system.

So you take no risk by reading this book. You will learn about your nervous system's quirks and superpowers so that it quits messing with your life. You will discover a possible lower brain connection (and what that may mean to you), as well as how this variable can affect restoring a nervous system's flexibility. You will quickly glean a myriad of simple ways to stay calm and grounded.

Together, that information puts you on the path to an easier life, with a reliable road map in hand. That way, you can keep moving along, following this path to wherever it may take you—including the possibility of experiencing wildly amazing changes that you never dreamed possible.

PART 1

Our Nervous System: Features, Nuances, and Hiccups

1

WHAT WE MAY NOT REALIZE

I f we want an easier life, we first need to become acquainted with our nervous system. That means we need to know about its mind-blowing capabilities, as well as the ways it can inadvertently sabotage us. A nervous system left to its own devices—where we remain in the dark on how it works—is one that will likely generate never-ending stress. So this chapter underscores a stark reality: Our nervous system is at play no matter what we're doing or wherever we are—including when we're on vacation.

My 22-year-old niece and her friend are having a great time while vacationing in Mexico. On this evening, they are walking back to their hotel after dining out. But suddenly a man jumps in front of them and tries to grab my niece's purse.

My niece immediately starts making wild moves (that she apparently recalls from a Girl Scout self-defense course when she was 10) as she yells at the top of her lungs, "Ayuda! Ayuda!"—the Spanish word for help.

But her friend is frozen. She is literally doing nothing.

Now, if we were filming this (true) scene as part of a documentary on the nervous system, there would be a lot to unpack here.

First, my niece and her friend are both responding to this threat—just in different ways. With lots of adrenaline pumping through my niece, she is now amped to fight her predator. But her friend is frozen. If another friend had been with them, and she had chosen to flee that scene, then our documentary would have shown each of the basic, instinctive reactions to a threat (which, in this case, was the purse snatcher).

But what if our nervous system assesses that fighting, fleeing, and freezing are not going to keep us safe from the imminent threat? Well, as our nervous system's last-ditch effort to protect us, we now go numb as we check out and dissociate from whatever is happening.

Yet here's what is often glossed over. We have zero say in *which* of those reactions protect us in any given situation. Sure, my niece enjoys telling her Mexico-attempted-purse-snatching story, since she likes how she is portrayed as a tough young woman who's not going to give up her purse.

However, she's less likely to tell the story of when she was home alone at age 11, just a few days before Christmas. That is when she peered through the window and saw Santa standing at her front door, ringing the doorbell.

Well, this Santa also triggered her memory of that same Girl Scout self-defense class. Only this time, my niece recalled how her instructors warned her to be wary of suspicious-looking people at the front door. So she was now in full-blown protection mode.

Fleeing to the bathroom, she grabbed the towel rack as her weapon and locked the door behind her. And that's when I got the panic call to come and rescue her from the "predator Santa" in her front yard. (As a side note, Santa was a family friend. My niece's dad was in the hospital, so this friend thought dressing up to deliver his gifts would bring a little extra holiday cheer.)

But back to the purse-snatching scene. It turns out that my niece's wild defense moves were effective because that guy now ran off, empty-handed. And yet the story does not end there—as is often the case after we've shifted into protection mode.

WHAT COMES NEXT

Like I said, my niece framed that memory as "I'm a don't-mess-with-me kind of chick," taking full credit for saving the day. After all, she had no clue what role her *nervous system* played in that event.

But neither did her friend—the one who froze. She just stood there, doing nothing, while someone tried to steal her friend's purse. How can she reconcile that response or spin it in a way that makes *her* look good (like my niece did)? She cannot.

So, what does the brain do when it doesn't understand why we have responded in a certain way? Well, it concocts a story—more accurately, it comes up with a whopper—to meet its need to fill in those gaps. And that is why my niece's friend created this story: "Mexico is not safe."

I say that because shortly thereafter, my niece's friend claimed that she was never going back to Mexico—and she hasn't since then. It will not matter if statistics show that there is an even greater incidence of purse snatching *in her hometown* than where they were vacationing, or if people point out that she was not physically harmed, or that the guy never even successfully stole anyone's purse.

Chances are that the wannabe thief also doesn't understand the nervous system. How is *he* going to spin what happened? After all, he fled from two young females, one who froze and the other who was trying to recreate moves that she had learned in a Girl Scout self-defense class over a decade earlier.

Yet once we understand the nervous system, there is only one accurate, short story for my niece, her friend, and even the unsuccessful thief—in truth, for all of us—whenever we have responded with a fight, flight, or freeze reaction. That story starts and ends with: Once upon a time, my nervous system assessed a threat, and then it decided the best way to protect me.

There is nothing more. That is the whole story.

Sure, as far as stories go, it is an admittedly boring one. Yet that dull, uncharged story still gives the brain an answer—which is all it wanted in the first place. But, best of all, that story negates the need to fabricate something else that we end up believing is true—and then often carry with us for the rest of our life.

THE WHAT IFS

For those who have read or heard about a dramatic event and then claimed with great bravado, "I would have done this or that"—here's the truth: None of us can predict how we might respond. When it comes to risk assessments, our nervous system always decides how we will initially react. That's why there's also no point in debating which protective-mode reaction is better than another.

For example, my niece's aggressive moves could have also easily backfired. What if her wild arm movements had angered the perpetrator, prompting him to physically attack her? Or what if he had then pulled a gun?

In such case, we might view her friend's freezing in a different light. Yes, the perpetrator would have snatched my niece's purse. But when considering all other possible ways that situation could have escalated from a fight response, her friend's freezing—doing nothing at all—was also a credible protective reaction.

OUR OVER-THE-TOP NERVOUS SYSTEM

The survival part of our nervous system takes its job quite seriously, to the point that it could even be viewed as obsessive and melodramatic.

For example, morning, noon, and night, this part is always fixated on whether we are safe or not—or in more theatrical terms, whether *we are going to die*—at any given moment. Granted, that is a lot of pressure, which may explain why our nervous system screws up, like a lot, by mostly sounding false alarms.

For example, suppose my nervous system sees a coiled cobra, and so it immediately shifts me into survival mode. Every part of my body is now ready to protect me from this threat. And, yes, those physiological changes are going to be most helpful—potentially even lifesaving—noting that a cobra's single bite can deliver enough neurotoxins to kill an elephant.

But guess what? It turns out that the curled-up object is *not* a cobra. It's just some coiled rope lying on the ground. Yet that realization comes a little too late in that my whole body has already prepared for the impending doom.

However, this is what is important to note. My new insight (I'm looking at a harmless rope and not a venomous cobra) is not enough *for my body* to immediately bounce back to how it was moments ago. The body—which undergoes an immediate myriad of physical changes once a stress reaction is triggered—must receive a visceral, convincing "text" that the threat *has* been resolved. Words alone will not get this job done.

Now, there's a good chance we already know that it has never helped to tell someone to relax when they were stressed. For example, after others have told us, "Calm down," when did we ever say, "Oh, I feel so much better now." Or, when people have assured us, "You're okay," when did we ever say, "Wow, you're right!" More likely, such comments just made us even more upset.

It is also good to remember that our nervous system is not going to change. It will continue to be melodramatic and overly protective about our potential demise. That means it will keep screwing up far more times than not, since most of us do not face much true danger in our life.

Our nervous system additionally assesses anything that might potentially separate us from "our pack" as a viable threat. Here's why: Each of us has a primordial, innate need to be with other humans. So, what happens when a neighbor directs a snarky comment at us? Or we discover that we're not invited to the holiday party? Or our boss criticizes us in front of our peers? Or anything else on a long list of what happens in our daily life? We often experience the same physiological stress reaction for those situations as we would if a tiger were truly about to attack us. After all, if we interpret others' actions as telling us, "You do not belong," we could be left all alone on the savanna. And we know that we will never survive without our pack.

Also, good luck expecting that our nervous system will ever reflect on its trigger-happy stress reaction or show remorse over all its errors. Hardly. In fact, if our nervous system could talk, it would never say something like, "Oops. Sorry about that. I'll do better next time." Or if I were ever to ask my nervous system to be more discerning (this supposes that we can engage in two-way conversations), I suspect that it would retort with some definite attitude, more along the lines of "Hey, how about saying, 'Job *well done*'? You're still alive, right?"

And yet, from a survival view, that attitude makes perfect sense. If the nervous system is wrong—like it ends up just being a coiled rope and not a cobra—a ramped-up physical reaction seems like a small price to pay *for keeping us alive*. Alternatively, if the nervous system errs when there *is* a true threat—like it decided it was just rope, but it ends up being a cobra—well, *that* has life-threatening consequences.

So shifting into protection mode is never going to be newsworthy. But that's why knowing how to bounce back is key to having a flexible nervous system and to ensuring that we don't get stuck in protection mode.

ITS SUPERPOWER SPEED

Our nervous system has an incredible ability to assess a risk in a split second. That is ridiculously, mind-bogglingly fast—far faster than how our conscious mind could evaluate a risk. That's why in terms of risk assessment, our conscious mind is never going to be in the same superpower league as our nervous system.

And recall that our nervous system has an unrelenting, laser-focus agenda to keep us safe. So there is no way our nervous system is ever going to pause to consult with the s-l-o-w, higher centers of our brain. We truly are at the mercy of whatever *our nervous system*—not our conscious mind—assesses as danger.

It is worth pausing a moment to let that fact sink in.

Of course, it's one thing to know that reality about our nervous system and another to see its speed played out in real time. While it was never my intention to participate in such a blatant unplanned experiment, that is exactly what happened to me.

For my entire life, I've always had normal blood pressure readings. That is, until the time I am late for a doctor's appointment and have to race across the large parking lot to my doctor's office.

I've barely checked in when the medical assistant calls me and takes my blood pressure. For the first time ever, it is high. But I explain it away by sharing how I have just been running. Yet when the doctor enters the room a bit later, she wants to take my blood pressure again. It is still high.

At this point, an alarming thought comes to mind: My mom died from a possible heart problem that she knew nothing about. But since my second blood pressure numbers are not that over-the-top high, my doctor just gives me some diet guidelines—all of which I already do.

I do not think any more about this doctor visit until about two years later, when I decide I should probably take my blood pressure.

After all, I haven't had a reading since that visit. So I order a machine from Amazon, with no clue of what is about to happen once it arrives.

As soon as I place my newly purchased blood pressure machine on my kitchen table, I notice that my heart is pounding. At first, I'm somewhat amused by what is going on. My nervous system has clearly recalled my high readings at my last checkup and my mom's heart history. So it has immediately assessed this simple machine from Amazon as a threat to me.

Since I want an accurate reading, I look away from the machine and start doing the many calming techniques I've learned. It takes a few minutes before I feel a notable shift.

Yet, as soon as I turn to see the blood pressure machine, my heart starts pounding all over again. I am surprised by the intensity of my body's reaction. After all, I speak in front of hundreds of people without my heart ever sounding a peep. But apparently just the mere sight of a small blood pressure machine is now enough to wreak havoc on my nervous system and consequently on my body.

Two more times, I look away and do a series of calming techniques for five minutes or so—only to get instantly triggered the minute I set eyes on the machine. It clearly does matter that my higher centers of the brain know exactly what is going on. My nervous system is not listening as it continues to sound the alarm.

Well, I am no longer amused. I need to take my blood pressure and move on to something else in my day.

I finally decide that I should just do it—and expect that the first test will be skewed. But if I think my heart is pounding loudly by looking at the machine, it's like a cacophony of the loudest hearts in the world as soon as I push the "on" button and the cuff begins to tighten around my arm.

After what seems like forever, that first test ends. I look at my numbers: 159/75. While not paramedic bad, certainly not good. But hopefully those numbers are low enough for my nervous system to take note and reconsider that I am not about to die.

It takes me two more repetitions of doing five minutes of calming techniques and then taking my blood pressure before the third
test reads 120/80—my normal blood pressure numbers. Finally.

THE EQUALIZER

How does my unplanned blood pressure demonstration apply to all
of us?

For starters, it does not matter whether we are a queen, a rock
star, a billionaire, homeless, young or old, or live in the city or the
country—our nervous system works the same way no matter who
we are. That's why none of us can escape this part of our biology:
Once we shift into protection mode, our rational and analytical
parts of our brain go immediately offline.

Recall that I *intellectually* knew that my blood pressure machine
was my trigger—and I even knew why. Yet those logical thoughts
had zero bearing on my nervous system's determination to protect
me or my body's physiological response to danger.

While my nervous system was hung up on a cheap blood pressure machine from Amazon, we are also all the same in that *anything*
can trigger our nervous system. That goes far beyond just something
we see. We can equally be triggered by a sound or smell, a tone
of voice, a facial expression, a posted sign, a song, a thought—the
point is that our nervous system is open to considering anything as
a potential threat.

We are also all the same in that our bodies undergo physiological changes to brace for the imminent threat. Of course, our body's
response is not always as notable as my heart-pounding reaction
to my blood pressure machine. In fact, that was rare for me since
that's not how my body usually braces once I'm triggered. But
whether we feel a tightening in our chest, a tingling on our face,
a gut punch, or any other subtle or overt physical sensation, the
message is always the same. These physical changes are our nervous

system's way of telling us that it has already assessed a threat and that it has ensured that our body is braced and prepared for whatever might come next.

IT'S NOT PERSONAL—AND YET IT IS

While it may often seem like it, our nervous system is not trying to mess up our life. Going in and out of connection mode and protection mode is simply our nervous system doing its job. It's never personal. It's biology, much in the same way that we can expect the tide to go in and out each day. That's what oceans do, right?

Yet when it comes to the tide, we seem to accept those fluctuations as part of nature. For example, if the high tide prevents us from walking along the shore, we do not cast blame on the ocean or now view ourselves as a victim by thinking, "Of course, it is high tide *now*, since this is when I planned to walk."

However, we can also say that the nervous system *is* very personal. That's because our nervous system scans our entire history—and no one else's—every time it makes a risk assessment. That is about as personal as it gets. That also explains why telling someone else that everything is okay usually backfires. My triggers are not necessarily yours.

For example, if my nervous system could talk, I imagine it yelling at whoever challenged its risk assessment, saying something like, "Maybe *your* nervous system came up empty-handed, but I just checked off ten boxes for Nancy! So back off—and let me do my job!"

Like it or not, this is how each of our nervous systems works. We have no option to shop around for one with different features that are more compatible with our life. Yet we can help our nervous system become our friend and ally. But first we just need to get to know it better, including understanding all its nuances and quirks.

And what if we do not ever get acquainted with our nervous system? Well, then there is a high probability we'll become stuck in protection mode. As you'll learn in the following chapter, that is a scenario we want to avoid.

2

〰〰〰〰

WHY WE DO NOT WANT TO BE STUCK IN PROTECTION MODE

Whether we go with a fight, flight, or freeze reaction, the response is always supposed to be temporary—just long enough to keep us safe until the threat is gone. Animals in the wild have this system down.

Take the gazelle. She may have just experienced a life-or-death chase from a predator looking for lunch. Or she may have been lying perfectly still on the ground (to appear dead) so that her predator would lose interest in her "dead" carcass.

Either way, once the threat is eliminated, the gazelle (literally) shakes off the entire episode. It never crosses her mind to spin a story like, "See, I'm always a victim." She never thinks to blame other gazelles or herself for what just happened. She certainly does not feel ashamed of the way she reacted while being threatened. And that's why, moments later, our lovely gazelle is now back to her leisurely, grass-grazing self.

But as humans—well, we often get stuck in protection mode.

SHOWING UP IN PROTECTION MODE

Many of us may not realize that we are stuck in protection mode. But that was how we viewed Sara, a participant in our family program. In that program, parents and their kids each change their own brain and nervous system. But they also engage in many activities with one another. While Sara did not resist making her own changes, she was often overtly combative about participating in the parent-child activities.

> Once again, Sara is unabashedly expressing her views. Her tone is abrupt and, yes, rather aggressive. However, I do not judge Sara or take her comments personally. I do not actually even think she senses she is resistant whenever she makes comments like "Why would I ever do *that* with my son? No way!"
>
> I also know that if I push and challenge Sara to change her thinking right then and there, she will just resist more. Her nervous system will only hear my words as another threat. I also do not issue an all-or-nothing ultimatum for Sara to do those activities with her son. Taking that approach would mean that I, too, have now shifted into protection mode in reaction to her resistance.
>
> Instead, I choose to focus on how Sara is diligently changing her own brain. I decide to let go that she refuses to participate in the many fun ways to interact with her son.
>
> Well, it's now the sixth week of our program, and Sara pulls me aside. She appears worried and proceeds to tell me that she's concerned about what has been going on with her. When I ask her to elaborate, she tells me what she has been experiencing.
>
> As I'm listening to her, I start to smile. "Sara," I say, "you're describing feeling calm. You have been feeling calm." Confused, she pauses for a moment and then snaps at me, "Well, I don't like it!"

Sara's initial, antagonistic reaction to feeling calm made sense. After all, she'd been living in protection mode for the longest time. She perceived hypervigilance and reactivity as normal and familiar. And that was why Sara's nervous system now assessed *feeling calm* as a threat.

This story has a happy ending, though. As the course continued, Sara no longer resisted feeling relaxed. At times, we even saw her smile during class. Yet Sara was still not doing any of the parent-child activities with her son.

Then, on the last day of class, Sara approached me. In a calm voice, she sincerely asked me, "Could I repeat the course again—but this time, do it for my son?"

In truth, most Brain Highways participants are stuck in protection mode when they first begin our program. Yet that isn't how they see themselves when they enroll. Parents in our family program typically think they've enrolled in the course for a son or daughter who has been struggling. They are simply game to also change their own brain and nervous system alongside their child. And yet so often around the second or third week of the program, a mom or dad will say, "You know, I think I have been in protection mode most of my life! I thought I was doing this program for my kid. But now I think this is even more for me!"

WHAT MAKES IT CHALLENGING

When we remain in a long-term unhealthy relationship, we do not necessarily stay because we believe it's good for us. Rather, we stay because it's what we know. Plus, it would take a lot of energy to leave and even more energy to start all over again with the unknown. And those same reasons are pretty much in line with why some people subconsciously choose to stay in protection mode.

I've also had Brain Highways participants initially share this fear: They believe that if they do not get ramped up to get something done, whether at work or elsewhere, they will lose their competitive edge. In other words, they fear that living a life outside protection mode may make them too complacent. Of course, that is just a story their brain concocted to explain their recurring adrenaline-rush behavior. But if they are attached to that story, they will not be persuaded by knowing that our physiology changes in protection mode in ways that now make us *less* efficient, as compared to undertaking that same task while in connection mode.

However, here's what is always going on. Whether we consciously decide to change our brain or not, it is continuously adapting. Now, sometimes those changes are great. But if we have been hanging out in protection mode for a long time, that is not the case. Unfortunately, we have no editor to ensure that all changes will be *helpful* neural connections. So sometimes a change is more accurately a *maladaptation* (though to our brain, all changes are merely reflections of whatever is going on in our life).

For example, if our life is one where we constantly feel overwhelmed, worried, and stressed, then our physiology will now change to match that lifestyle. In such cases, our amygdala—a key part of the whole trigger-the-alarm process—becomes physically larger. However, this is one of those times where bigger is not better. The bigger the amygdala, the more reactive it becomes.

And there's more. The parts of the brain responsible for memory, learning, and impulse control now also shrink in size. Great—that means we have literally changed our physiology so that protection mode is now our default way of being.

Thankfully, there is also good news here. When we understand the process, it's equally possible to reverse all those maladaptive changes.

PROTECTION MODE IN DISGUISE

Once we become aware of protection mode, it's not rocket science to conclude that someone has shifted into this reactive state whenever someone is swearing, yelling, acting aggressively, having a meltdown, experiencing a panic attack, or exhibiting some other stress reaction. Yet we are also in protection mode if our brain and nervous system have lost their ability to *differentiate*. That's because everything in life is always changing. So our brain and nervous system need to be able to make reliable comparisons to know how best to respond.

That's why a well-regulated nervous system and brain can easily discern differences in our daily experiences. For example, we can effortlessly note changes in our emotions, in people's facial expressions, in someone's tone of voice, and more. Such a brain and nervous system can also ponder differing perspectives without immediately reacting as though contrary views must be a threat.

But once we can no longer easily differentiate, we narrow our view of the world. From a biological, survival perspective, that makes sense. When there's a true threat, there is no room for any gray area. Everything *has to be* black or white. Think about it. If we stopped to consider a spectrum of ways to view a dangerous situation, we would not survive.

Yet those who claim to be proud skeptics, perfectionists, all-the-time-serious people, and always-on-the-go folks may have unknowingly adopted that same no-gray-area mindset. While these groups of people do not likely view themselves as being in protection mode, their inability to differentiate will influence how they respond in parts of their everyday life. For example, self-identified skeptics will now find it difficult to differentiate between those who *are* making fraudulent claims and those who are merely presenting innovative ideas. They will also no longer be able to see the difference between opting to pass on a product merely because it doesn't resonate with them and automatically refusing to consider something because it's new and unfamiliar. To the skeptic, everyone and everything has become suspect. That is because the skeptic's brain has now become wired to view the world as someone always being out to "get" them.

Perfectionists, all-the-time-serious people, and always-on-the-go folks also make decisions related to how they are no longer differentiating in parts of their life. For example, perfectionists can no longer differentiate between those times that going with the flow (even if not ideal) will keep everyone connected and times when it may be beneficial to put more structure in place before moving forward. They can no longer differentiate between times when putting forth a good effort—and being done and content with such work—is enough and times when more revision is needed and warranted. Instead, there is always only one view: perfection.

In a similar way, all-the-time-serious people can no longer discern when to be lighthearted and playful from when to be solemn and pensive. So they remain serious and do not have much fun in their life. Since always-on-the-go folks cannot differentiate between when to be active and when to be restful, they then remain on overdrive and do not relax.

Of course, such people often explain away their actions by saying, "Well, that's just who I am"—as though they were born a skeptic or a perfectionist, or that their DNA makes them serious and on-the-go all the time. But by remaining attached to such identities, their nervous system now needs to be on high alert (whether they are aware of this or not). They cannot let their guard down because whatever they fear might happen may very well come to pass (or so their nervous system has become wired to believe). And that ongoing fear is what creates the perfect setup for being stuck in protection mode.

THE FREEZE REACTION

Sometimes the nervous system decides that remaining perfectly still or silent protects us in that moment. As with the gazelle who plays dead to fool her predator, this kind of protective reaction makes sense to humans also.

For example, suppose a father is yelling and berating his son for knocking over a glass of water. Well, if the son reacts by defending what he did or by running away from his father, he might make an already bad situation worse. On the other hand, being quiet and still reduces the risk of angering his father even more, which is why freezing in this situation is a helpful, protective response (from the nervous system's view).

However, what if the father regularly berates and belittles his son? In such case, the son's nervous system may conclude that the basic fight, flight, and freeze reactions are not going to protect him. So the nervous system takes the original freeze response even further, and the son automatically shuts down and withdraws from the present whenever his father comes at him.

This version of the freeze response is also protective because the son can now dissociate from the emotional pain that comes with experiencing his father's wrath. This kind of detachment can be so effective that such people may even think they are fine—even though they are in protection mode.

Initially, I did not understand this "checking out" behavior among some of the parents who came with their kids to participate in classes at the Brain Highways Center. While the parents of this "checking out" group were enrolled in different classes through-out the years, they particularly piqued my interest because they held jobs that demanded such a strong presence when they were at work. These were emergency room doctors, nurses, ministers, police officers, prosecutors, and more. Yet when it came to inter-acting with their kids, many of these parents were like deer in the headlights. The following scene (or some variation of it) is what I would often observe.

Through the window, I see Sam and his dad. Along with the other families, they are waiting for us to open the door so they can enter for their class.

While I know that Sam's dad is a prominent prosecutor, that information is now jarring with what I'm observing through the window. This well-known prosecutor's four-year-old son is forcefully punching his dad's leg—again and again. Yet the prosecutor appears listless, like he is barely there, even as his son becomes more upset. He never tells his son to stop hitting, let alone move away from him.

I'm confused by what I'm seeing. I find myself thinking, "If Sam's dad shows up in court with that same demeanor, a lot of criminals are going free." And yet I know that this prosecutor cannot do that and keep his job. So what's going on here?

Well, now I understand that detaching can be a protective-mode response. Over time, dissociating can even become an automated stress reaction. For example, this prosecutor had already experienced (many times) that he could not calm his son. That realization triggered repeated feelings of frustration, helplessness, and despair. After all, no matter what he tried, nothing ever changed. That's why the prosecutor's nervous system now automatically protected him from that predicable emotional pain. If he simply "checked out" whenever his son was upset, he would no longer have to feel those agonizing emotions.

The problem, though, is that buried emotions are still there. So, while people who dissociate from stressful events may even insist that they are not bothered by what has happened, their body (if it could talk) would say otherwise. That's why I think the title of Bessel van der Kolk's book *The Body Keeps the Score* is brilliant. When a threat is not resolved, the body stays involved even if the mind has checked out.

FALLOUT FROM A FREEZE REACTION

Suppose a principal shows up to do a surprise evaluation of a woman named Emily when she is teaching a math lesson to her high school students—and she freezes when she sees him. Yes, freezing here could be embarrassing. It may cause the principal to think that Emily lacks confidence. It may even result in a poor evaluation.

But the potential fallout in this situation is never going to be the same as when a police officer, paramedic, doctor, or someone in the military freezes in a volatile, high-stress situation while on the job. After all, immobilization here might even inadvertently cause someone to die.

However, the nervous system has no clue about our profession, and it's never thinking about *someone else's safety* when it chooses a protective response for us. Yet, without understanding that freezing is a biological protective-mode reaction, some professionals may experience overwhelming shame over their inaction. They don't understand how their immobilization was intended to protect them. If such professionals also lose their job or others harshly criticize their inaction, that shame only increases as they remain in protection mode.

Over the years, we've met such participants in our Brain Highways program. Upon learning about the nervous system, these participants begin to understand what happened to them *from a biological perspective.* This new knowledge then gives them a different way to frame their inaction, which also helps them be kinder to themselves.

Such knowledge can also be helpful to rape victims. Regrettably, while these women already suffer greatly from being violated in this brutal, abhorrent way, some are additionally tormented if they froze while being attacked. That's because they and others know that not all women respond that way. Many will fight off their attacker—and with great ferocity.

So the women who freeze are sometimes viewed with skepticism. (If you were really raped, why did you just lie there and do nothing?) These same women are also often "raped" again in the courtroom as the defense lawyer keeps hammering on how the woman did nothing to resist. There is no mention that the woman's nervous system made the decision to freeze and then dissociate from the terrifying threat after concluding that none of the basic fight or flight responses were going to protect her.

DOOMED DECISION-MAKING

As soon as we are in protection mode, the higher centers of our brain shut down. So it is always going to be in our best interest to *wait* to make any decision until we are back in connection mode. However, the basic neurobiology of protection mode often makes that challenging to do. That reality ended up creating lots of stress for Mac and his family.

Mac is excited about his new promotion. That is why he doesn't think about his three prior coworkers who already quit this job over a notably short period of time.

However, once Mac begins the job, he becomes distressed rather quickly. He is given a never-ending list of urgent, unrealistic deadlines. It doesn't matter that Mac keeps working overtime—every day. He's given more and more projects that need to be completed right now.

Three months into the job, Mac arrives at work and is reprimanded for not meeting one of these delusionary deadlines. He has had enough. He quits right then and there.

But here is the problem. Mac has no other job lined up and no other income. Yet he does have a sizable house mortgage, along with other bills to pay, and a family of four to feed. So Mac has basically traded stressors.

Mac's family and friends do not know how the nervous system works. That's why some of them now frame Mac as thoughtless or even selfish for making such a rash decision without considering how his action would affect his entire family.

Mac also does not know how the nervous system works. So he beats himself up for impulsively quitting his job without a plan and for being so stupid for taking the job in the first place. He knew—but chose to ignore—that there were big red flags. Ironically, such thoughts only keep Mac in protection mode, where he will likely continue to make poor decisions.

But what if Mac had waited to make his decision until he was out of protection mode? While there is no one answer, Mac may have reflected (a key word that shows we are in connection mode) that he would be the *fourth* person to quit if he, too, decided to leave the job. That key piece of information may have prompted Mac to meet with his supervisor to explain his concerns and to explore options that would meet everyone's needs. For example, maybe at this juncture (again, noting the current history of people quitting this job), his boss may have been amenable to adding one or two assistants to the team so that Mac could realistically meet deadlines.

And even if such a meeting did not go as Mac had hoped, he could have waited to quit until after he had secured another job. That would have eliminated all the subsequent stress he placed on his entire family with his quick flight reaction to quit without a plan in place.

However, once in protection mode, Mac's neurobiology made it challenging, if not impossible, for him to see the bigger picture. Surviving *that moment* (get me out of here!) was all his brain and nervous system were focused on.

Of course, that reaction is great if we are in true danger. But Mac's personal physical safety was not at risk when his boss reprimanded him. That's why, when there's no true danger, we always want to put any decision on hold until we're out of protection mode.

THE NARROW VIEW

When we are in protection mode, we're wired to have tunnel vision—which makes perfect sense from a survival view. After all, if a tiger is about to attack us, it's not in our best interest to also be concerned about the *tiger*, as in how he might be having a rough time out on the savanna, or it may have been days since he has had a good meal.

When we're in survival mode, *it is always only about us*. No one else matters at that moment. Logic and rational thinking are also MIA, meaning that none of us are the easiest people to interact with (or even like) once in protection mode. However, we unfortunately are still able to talk—and now everything we say reflects our narrow, I-am-the-only-person-who-matters view.

Yet once we understand how that narrow view is part of a protection-mode response, we may find ourselves pausing as we think about people we know who we have written off as rude, self-centered, and uncaring. Instead, it's possible that such people have been stuck in protection mode, where they see the world only as a place with never-ending danger.

WHEN INTERACTIONS GO SOUTH

Once in protection mode, we may hear and process information quite differently than when we're in connection mode. For starters, our ears are now primed to be attuned to potential predator sounds instead of the higher vibration of human voices. To be clear—this doesn't mean that we can no longer hear people speaking when we're in protection mode. It's just that *how we interpret what they're saying* is often distorted.

For example, suppose a mother tells her son, "Jake, pick up your toys." Now, everyone in that room concurs that Jake's mother's tone was soft and neutral when she said that. Yet Jake screams back, *"I am picking up my toys!"* That's because Jake "heard" his mom's simple direction as a threat—as though she *had* yelled, "Jake, *pick up your toys!*" So to protect himself from this perceived threat, Jake's reaction is both defensive and combative.

Or (also a true story) a dad nonchalantly asks his teenage daughter, "Mia, when I'm at the deli, would you like me to pick up a salad for you?" But Mia responds in an accusatory voice, "I can't believe you just called me fat!"

Now, in both cases, it's pointless to try and correct what Jake or Mia think they heard. To Jake, his mom *did* yell at him. To Mia, her father *did* just call her fat. Any challenge—at that moment—will only prompt Jake and Mia to double down on their position.

Of course, any of us can hear distortedly anywhere, at any time. For example, suppose a husband and wife are at a doctor's appointment to get the wife's tests results. After revealing some alarming lab numbers, the doctor shares that the wife needs to make some significant lifestyle changes "or she could be dead in a year." But the wife, who was already in protection mode as soon as she heard the results, does not process the words *or* and *could*. Instead, she hears that she *will* be dead in a year. Nothing her husband says in the car ride home convinces her otherwise. She knows what she heard the doctor say!

When we are in protection mode, more than only our ability to process information is off. A person's neutral tone, facial expression, and gestures can also be misinterpreted as somehow threatening—and so we react in kind.

That's why being stuck in protection mode is also going to greatly interfere with having good relationships. For starters, people may now avoid us because they have grown weary of walking on eggshells whenever they're in our company. They never know how we are going to react. Or they have given up on us altogether after too many experiences when we acted in a distorted, combative way.

But it is not supposed to be that hard to read the room. We all have *neuroception*, an innate process that helps us read safety and danger cues accurately without conscious awareness. However, once we are in protection mode, our neuroception becomes skewed. Now, nothing is safe. Now, everyone and everything is a potential threat, which is why we then react the way we do.

LEARNING DOES NOT HAPPEN

It makes sense that we cannot learn *and* be in protection mode at the same time. In the first place, why would my brain care about fractions, or the Civil War, or how to use a new computer program if my nervous system has already sounded the alarm that I am about *to die*?

Then there are those physiological changes that come with protection mode. For example, my eyes are going to dilate as part of that process. However, dilated eyes will make it difficult to focus on whatever is in near view, noting that words on a page or screen may now even blur. So forget reading and writing with ease whenever we're in protection mode.

And recall that I am also likely to distort some or much of whatever my teacher says when I'm braced for a potential threat. But this is where we really pause. The higher centers of the brain—on which we must rely to learn—are always *offline* whenever we're in protection mode.

THERE IS MORE

At this point, you may be thinking, "Hey, I get it. Protection mode is not great. So why not just tell me how to get out of protection mode right now?" I do understand that sentiment, and I promise that you will learn how to do that.

Yet, from a brain's view, awareness is always a prerequisite to changing what we do. That new awareness is what catches our brain's attention, helping us "see" ourselves, others, and life in general quite differently than before.

That's why we want to first understand all the ways that our nervous system might be interfering with our relationships, especially with those we love the most. While this chapter touches on some ways that protection mode causes problems in our interactions with others, there's more.

We want to know how we may have inadvertently created a disconnect with others. We want to understand how others may have unknowingly created a disconnect with us. Then, with that understanding and awareness, we're ready to learn about connection mode—what that really means and how we land there. In Chapter 3, you'll continue to learn how, once again, our biology keeps showing up in our lives in ways we haven't previously considered.

3

~~~~~~

HOW OUR NERVOUS SYSTEM
SKEWS RELATIONSHIPS

When choosing a partner, we often hear that "opposites attract." But that belief takes on a new meaning if partners also react to stress in completely different ways.

SURGERS AND DORSAL DIVERS

Suppose that one partner of a couple is what we fondly call at Brain Highways a *surger*. When surgers are stressed, they are amped, ready to fight or flee from a potential threat. That's because their stress reaction comes with lots of adrenaline rushing through their body. That's also why surgers predictably react to stress with *urgency*, as though the house was on fire. ("We need to do something *now!*") Over time, this surging becomes automated, so that it is now the surger's automatic stress reaction.

In contrast, the other partner may be what we fondly call at Brain Highways a *dorsal diver*. The word *dorsal* refers to the part of our nervous system that initiates physiological changes to shut down specific body systems. The word *dive* describes the action of shutting down. Another simple image for a dorsal diver is a turtle retreating to its shell to block out the external world.

When stressed, dorsal divers literally freeze, briefly unable to speak. Or they appear very still, almost as though they are temporarily paralyzed, like a deer in the headlights. If this kind of immobilization does not resolve the threat, dorsal divers will then dissociate and withdraw from the current stressful situation. In such cases, their bodies undergo changes that make it possible to "check out" and bypass emotional or physical pain. These physiological changes explain why dorsal divers predictably react to stress as though nothing is wrong. ("What problem? Everything is fine.") That's truly what they think.

But what happens if one partner is a surger and the other is a dorsal diver? Well, that's when we can predict with amazing accuracy how that couple is going to argue. In the following common scenario, Maya is the surger, and Ben is the dorsal diver. (Note that these roles could easily be reversed in another home.) In this scenario, neither Maya nor Ben knows anything about the nervous system, let alone that surgers and dorsal divers react quite differently to stress.

It's the end of the day, and Ben and Maya have just received an email from their six-year-old's teacher. She lets them know that their son is now reading below grade level.

Well, Maya (the surger) has already begun to react, as her mind immediately races to the future. If her son can't read, then he's going to do poorly in school! If he does poorly in school, he won't get into a good college! If he doesn't get into a good college, he won't land a good job! If he doesn't find a good job, he'll be living at home forever!

Ben's nervous system is also time-traveling at lightning speed. But it goes right to the time that Ben was in elementary school and spent long hours in remedial programs that never yielded much improvement. That memory is more than enough for Ben's nervous system to sound the alarm. However, since Ben's conscious mind was not involved in that assessment, he is unaware that he does a dorsal dive to protect himself from feeling that pain all over again.

So everything is set for two dueling stress reactions to take centerstage.

Maya is already starting to rattle off a list of things that she insists they need to do *right now* to bring their son up to speed. But Ben has already checked into his turtle shell.

However, Maya knows nothing about dorsal diving, which is why she interprets Ben's lack of response as evidence that he does not care. His (alleged) indifference makes Maya surge even more. Of course, the more she tries to engage Ben, the more he retreats.

Since Maya's nervous system is viewing this stressful situation (and all stress) as though their house is *on fire*, she clearly cannot fight those flames alone. This is a life-threatening situation!

That means she is not giving up on enlisting Ben's help.

Since Maya will not stop talking, Ben now pokes his head out of his shell to fling a good, inflammatory zinger right at her. Yes, it stings, but Maya is thinking, "Well, at least that's better than his silence. He's back!"

Except Ben is not back. That dorsal diver "punch" is just a quick, desperate reaction to get the surger to shut up. Before Maya blinks, Ben has already retreated into his shell once again.

Maya is now thinking, *"No way! You get back out here!"* But that is not going to happen. Nothing about their son's current reading situation gets resolved that evening.

When it's finally time to go to bed, Maya is still time-traveling to her son's bleak future (that she must prevent from ever becoming true). She happens to look over at Ben's side of the bed. *"What? He's already asleep! How can he sleep at a time like this?"*

Since Maya's nervous system is still pumping out adrenaline, she's wide awake. She continues to ruminate on the *reading level crisis*—which is now also being fueled with anger, frustration, and resentment. It is clearly up to her, all by herself, to save her son. Maya barely gets any sleep that night.

Ben, on the other hand, awakens the next morning feeling fresh and rejuvenated, acting as though there never was an email or that they were even arguing the night before. After all, his protective response has allowed him to shelve the threat that was triggered by the teacher's email.

So he smiles at Maya and says, "Good morning."

"Good morning?" Maya retorts with indignation. "Are you kidding me?"

With great predictability, round two of this fight has just begun.

CHANGING HOW WE FIGHT

What if we now view how we fight from the lens of the nervous system?

For starters, it will *not* move situations forward if, with our new knowledge, we now smugly call out the other person by saying something like, "You're just dorsal diving," or "You're just surging." Neither of those commentaries will be well received.

Yet the script does change if both people quickly recognize that they are in protection mode *and notice the way in which they are responding.* The surger may now think, "Oh, I am reacting like the house is on fire. Yes, I am upset, but there are no flying cinders, let alone flames, at this moment." In other words, surgers lose their credibility if they respond to every threat with the same over-the-top reaction.

Similarly, the dorsal diver may now think, "Oh, I am starting to retreat into my shell—and if I stay there, how will I know what is happening or if something changes?" In other words, dorsal divers lose their credibility if they automatically dismiss everything as no big deal. The truth is, sometimes surgers do accurately detect "smoke."

Ideally, if both the surger and the dorsal diver recognize that they have shifted into protection mode, they can use that awareness as feedback. That's why they both do various calming actions (such as those presented in Part 3) to return to connection mode as quickly as possible. Until that happens, everything else is tabled.

But what if just one of the two people returns to connection mode? Well, it's still going to be a different scene. For example, once in connection mode, the surger's prior amped energy is now contained, which may help reduce the dorsal diver's need to retreat. Being in connection mode also makes it easy to remember that gentle approaches (no pounding and rocking the dorsal diver's shell to force an exile) are what help dorsal divers feel safe to return to the world.

Or, once in connection mode, the dorsal diver is already going to reduce the surger's angst by not hiding out in the shell. That will be especially true if a surger also has a fear of flying solo. So to move forward, there is no "everyone-has-to-be-in-connection-mode" requirement.

To note, whenever I present these kinds of how-we-fight scenarios at Brain Highways, there are always some quiet chuckles, along with many "you got me" smiles. There is also lots of head turning toward a partner with an expression that says, "And that would be you." Keep in mind that our participants are from all over the world, so apparently, how we fight is pretty universal.

At one point of the class, I often get asked, "Can someone be both a surger and a dorsal diver?" The answer is yes. That's because our automated stress reactions are often those that were modeled for us as a child. If one parent is a surger and the other is a dorsal diver, a child may have downloaded and adopted both ways of reacting to stress.

I also get asked how someone who tends to do *flight* behavior responds in a fight. So if we return to the Maya and Ben scenario, let's say that Ben tends to flee instead of shutting down and dissociating. They're still going to end up disconnecting from each other, but *how* they arrive there will be different than if Ben was a dorsal diver. Here's how that version goes.

> Maya is surging and wants to discuss how they will fix the reading level crisis right away. Ben tells her that he is open to looking at options—just not at this moment. They will discuss it later (which is often code for "never" if someone tends to respond with flight behavior). But Maya's nervous system accepts and hears his response as "Help is on its way."
>
> Of course, after days go by and Ben has reason after reason for why it's not a good time to discuss this, Maya's surging protective reaction can no longer be contained. So the fight begins, starting with Maya accusing Ben of not keeping his word to discuss this problem.
>
> However, as soon as Maya starts challenging Ben's sincerity, he gets up to leave the room (another classic flight reaction). But Maya now follows him wherever he goes. She is going to get her fight, even if she has to keep following him from room to room. And since Maya is not backing down, at some point, Ben will fight back.

Our neurobiology is the reason that Ben ultimately switches from a flight to a fight reaction. Both flight and fight responses come from the same part of our nervous system. If the threat changes (as in Maya is now attacking Ben's integrity and refusing to leave him alone), it's easy to use that initial adrenaline rush to now fight the threat instead of trying to flee from it.

LAUGHING IN PROTECTION MODE

Of the three possible protective-mode reactions, dorsal diving is probably the most misunderstood—especially when laughter becomes part of that response.

At a family gathering, my mother-in-law is once again telling everyone the story of my husband when he was 12 years old. As is often the case with family folklore, she tells the story the same way each time.

Smiling, she says, "Well, earlier that afternoon, Jim falls and hurts his wrist while roller skating. But he doesn't tell us." More smiling as she continues, "Well, it's now midnight, and there's Jim waking me up, telling me how much his arm hurts. We take him to the emergency room, and it turns out that Jim has broken his wrist."

The story always ends with her chuckling, as if to say, "Isn't that the cutest story you ever heard?" Right on cue, everyone else in Jim's family also laughs, as they always do when hearing this story.

Now, back in those early days of our marriage, I knew nothing about our nervous system. But once we were alone, I would say to Jim, "You know, that's not really a funny story, right? I mean, it's more like a very sad story. You didn't even think that you could go to your parents when you first started experiencing all that pain?" And no surprise, Jim would just laugh.

It was only years later that I learned how laughing at odd (and by most standards inappropriate) times can be part of a dorsal diver's response. First, dorsal divers become conditioned to avoid feeling emotions. Yet not feeling sadness, or fear, or any other emotion in stressful situations does not mean that such emotions are not still showing up in the body. So some dorsal divers may come to rely on laughter as a defense mechanism to shield themselves from feeling whatever true emotions they are suppressing. In such case, laughing may release some of the nervous energy that comes from the dorsal diver's avoidance of feeling whatever has shown up.

As far as Jim's broken wrist story goes, it's possible that his mother's way of telling the story—smiling and chuckling—covers long-buried feelings if she unknowingly did a dorsal dive when Jim finally told her that he was in pain. If so, perhaps the dorsal dive protected her from feeling guilty or embarrassed that she hadn't noticed her son was significantly hurt or that he didn't ask for her help right away.

But then why does everyone else in the family—including Jim— also laugh whenever she shares that story? Well, Jim grew up in a home, like many homes, where emotions—other than anger— were rarely expressed. So it's no surprise that everyone in his family learned that laughing in uncomfortable situations was acceptable.

WHEN LAUGHING BACKFIRES

Laughing when someone is in emotional or physical pain does not go well. In fact, laughing during such times usually creates a huge disconnect between whoever is feeling the emotional or physical pain and whoever is doing the laughing.

Of course, most people have no idea that laughter might be a dorsal diver's reaction to shield true emotions. So people with low self-esteem may feel embarrassed whenever someone laughs at them when they're being emotional. They may worry that perhaps they *were* just making too big of a deal over whatever happened.

But more frequently, people simply frame the person who is laughing at such times as insensitive, tactless, uncaring, or just an all-time jerk. Before I understood the connection between dorsal diving and laughing, I confess that that's how I may have framed Jim whenever he laughed in the middle of emotionally tense situations. For example, there was the time when our youngest was a teen and was pouring her heart out to Jim.

Sobbing, she is trying to explain what has upset her. But that kind of emotional intensity—especially coming from his teenage daughter—is way too much for Jim's nervous system to handle. He doesn't know how to remain present in this kind of situation.

Instead, his nervous system responds exactly as it has been automated over the years. Jim does a dorsal dive to suppress whatever emotions are trying to surface. But our daughter is still distraught and continues to cry. And that's when Jim begins to laugh.

It probably goes without saying how she reacted to her father *laughing* at her emotional pain. But here's what's also awesome about changing our brain and nervous system. We often get a do-over, where we have a chance to respond to a similar situation in the future.

And so there was another time when our youngest was distressed—only now, this was after Jim had learned of his tendency to dorsal dive in emotional situations. It also happened after Jim had practiced tools to stay present when feeling discomfort.

Jim walks into the room and immediately sees his daughter crying. She turns to him and asks for a hug. Jim has no understanding of why she is upset. But this time, Jim does not laugh. Without saying a word, he embraces her with a long, comforting hug—which is exactly what she needs at that moment.

To note, kids can also be the ones who laugh as part of a dorsal dive reaction. At the start of our program, kids have often shared what seems like a humiliating or frightening story. But when these kids tell what happened, they're smiling and laughing as though the story is so funny.

For example, a teen was laughing as he shared a regular occurrence in his third-grade classroom. "Right before recess, my teacher used to walk over to my messy desk and turn it upside down so that everything fell all over the floor. Then she would smile and say, 'You need to stay in during recess to clean up this mess.' Everyone in the class would laugh."

But again, this teen was also laughing as he told this story many years later. My guess is that he probably laughed along with his classmates while doing a dorsal dive to dissociate from feelings of humiliation. However, since *that* part of the experience was still buried, he remembered the story only as being "funny."

Laughing in protection mode can have even more serious ramifications. In class one day, I had just explained the connection between laughing and dorsal diving to a group of parents. I noticed that a parent had raised her hand. While her face reflected a combination of horror and understanding, she clearly wanted to share something. I called on her, and she began to speak.

> "When I was growing up, my father physically abused my brother. But whenever my father would start to beat him, my brother would laugh. I used to think, 'No! Don't laugh!' since that would only enrage my father even more—and then he would hit my brother harder and harder. But my brother would just keep laughing."
>
> We see her tearing up. And then, in almost a whisper, she says, "Now I understand. When my brother laughed, it was his nervous system protecting him. It helped him bypass feeling the emotional pain of having a father who would inflict so much physical pain on his son."

WHEN DORSAL DIVING SPIRALS

If I were to introduce you to my mother-in-law, this is what you would come to know. While she is now 92, she was one of the first seniors to jump on social media when it took off. (Okay, maybe I exaggerate, but it seemed like it.) My mother-in-law is also someone who takes on a thousand-piece puzzle with zest, cooks vegan and gluten-free meals to accommodate family members' ever-changing diets (a far cry from her Betty Crocker cookbooks), rides an exercise bike, and sews incredible gifts for family members (donating much of what she sews, as well). She's also my number-one person to receive my favorite fiction thrillers once I'm done with them, since she remains an avid reader. That's my mother-in-law in connection mode, and I love and adore her.

But she has also mastered dorsal diving. Of course, that is my mother-in-law in protection mode. That's when she is wearing her full suit of armor, the one that protects her from feeling and expressing emotions.

I now know that suppressing emotions is a common protective-mode reaction. But, at times, I still feel sad and frustrated that my family and I have never been able to chink away at her armor.

However, I am grateful that my knowledge of the nervous system helps me view my mother-in-law with compassion whenever she is in protection mode. For starters, it stops the higher centers of my brain from concocting some story to try and make sense of her behavior. Instead, I remain curious.

For example, I've often pondered why my mother-in-law will not allow most emotions into her life. I sometimes think that something terrible must have happened when she was very young. Or someone must have hurt her so badly that her brain and nervous system processed that it was absolutely *not safe* to feel emotions, but she has no explicit memory of that happening (since that event would be buried in her subconscious mind). Or it may have been as simple as she learned to respond this way because that's what her mother modeled in their home, which was probably previously modeled by her mother's mother—and so it goes.

Yet by far, my father-in-law's horrific car accident probably best underscores my mother-in-law's unbelievable ability to dorsal dive.

It is raining, and my father-in-law is driving along the highway. My mother-in-law is sitting beside him in the passenger seat. Suddenly, a woman in the car behind them hits their pickup truck with great force. The truck spins sideways and starts to roll. As the truck now turns upside down, the top hits the asphalt, and the roof on my father-in-law's side crashes down on his head.

Miraculously, my mother-in-law is just bruised with a few sprained ribs, and so she stays in the hospital only that first night. But my father-in-law is in a coma, and he remains that way for nine long months. When he finally comes out of it, he is never the same.

His speech is now what can only be described as guttural sounds. He cannot walk. He cannot do simple functions to take care of himself, such as put on a shirt or wash his face. He basically lies on a bed, year after year.

But one would never suspect that anything significant has ever happened in my mother-in-law's life. When talking to her, she refers to my father-in-law as though he is a bit down with the flu. Her demeanor, though, is not to be confused with when we hold on to hope and keep a positive attitude in times of great challenges. This is dorsal diving because my mother-in-law suppresses every possible emotion related to the accident, as well as those related to her current reality. In truth, I do not know if she ever feels intense grief, anguish, despair, and sorrow over how their lives have changed so radically or if she ever allows herself to yearn for how their life used to be. I do know that she never shares or shows any of those emotions around us.

Yet I also have this thought. If not a dorsal dive, then what? My mother-in-law could just as easily surge and engage in power-over actions with anyone trying to help. Or she could bail altogether, leaving my father-in-law's care entirely up to the rest of us. After all, those are also protective reactions to a perceived threat.

But my mother-in-law is a seasoned dorsal diver. That's why it's easy for her to dissociate from the enormity of all that has happened, which means my father-in-law's condition does not deter her from spending time with him. Quite admirably, my mother-in-law is

never far from his side (for which we are all grateful) until he dies
14 years later.

While my mother-in-law's ongoing dorsal diving helped her
cope, it put Jim in an untenable position whenever he visited his
dad. This six-foot-one man used to ride motorcycles, fly airplanes,
race speedboats, install electrical wiring in hundreds of buildings,
and create amazing woodwork. But now, he just laid there, looking
at his son as though he did not even recognize him. For Jim, the stark
reality of his dad's condition was excruciating and heart-wrenching
while also surreal, since his mom would be cheerfully chatting away
at her husband's side.

With time, Jim understood that his mother's dissociative
response meant that she could not see or acknowledge his grief.
There was never going to be a time for them to comfort each other,
even though such connection is also part of our nervous system's way
to help us through intensely difficult challenges.

CLARIFYING

Once again, my mother-in-law's dorsal diving examples are only
snapshots of when she is in protection mode. That's not *who* she is.

So here is the first takeaway. None of us want to be judged—let
alone framed as that is *who we really are*—by those times when our
nervous system chooses to protect us. That holds true for however
we respond, whether we're doing deep dorsal diving or over-the-top,
wild surging.

Of course, that doesn't mean that our protective reactions do not
come with unintended ramifications. But we don't have to create
more of a disconnect by now passing judgment on someone else's
actions. We can always choose to stick to the boring story: Once
upon a time, the nervous system made a risk assessment and chose
a protective reaction.

It is also important to note that dorsal divers probably have no awareness of the pain they may inadvertently cause when wearing their armor. To be clear, I am 100 percent certain that my mother-in-law loves Jim, and she would never intentionally do anything to cause her son pain. I also know that she did her best under excruciating circumstances. It was an unbearable ordeal, one that would have wreaked havoc on anyone's nervous system—even those with a myriad of ways to shift out of protection mode. To judge or frame my mother-in-law otherwise would be totally missing the point of the examples I share.

True, she is a skilled dorsal diver. But that's hardly an anomaly, which is the main reason I introduce her to you. She could easily be your mother-in-law or your mother. She could be your father-in-law or your father. She could be your brother or your sister. She could be your own child. She could be your best friend. She could be you. That's why my mother-in-law's story is in this book.

In truth, I believe that all of us have dorsal dived at some point in our life. Since shutting down and dissociating from something too painful to bear are effective, primordial protection strategies, it's hard to imagine that our nervous system has *never* protected us that way.

I have also discovered that the more we learn about our nervous system, the more humbled we become. For example, once upon a time, I would have told you that I had never dorsal dived—that is, until I began addressing my own nervous system. To my surprise, I discovered that I had also buried emotions that were too painful to feel. But like every other dorsal diver, I just had no awareness of doing so at the time.

Once we understand the nervous system, it's clear that emotions are key to our survival in this world. And yet most of us are never taught anything about the neurobiology of emotions.

For starters, emotions are supposed to be more like visitors who arrive *and then leave* after they have shown up on our doorstep. After all, we don't expect visitors to camp out in our backyard indefinitely, let alone move into our basement. But if we do not greet emotions, observe them, and help them pass (if they need assistance to do so), we end up expending an inordinate amount of energy trying to keep them suppressed. And as you will discover in Chapter 4, all that effort won't even matter in the long run. One way or another, our buried emotions end up messing with our life.

We may have also misunderstood an important feature of our nervous system. At the time we initially dorsal dived, it *was* a great protective response. I say that with conviction because we clearly survived. To our nervous system, that's always going to mean victory. However, keeping those emotions buried *forever* is going rogue from our nervous system's intended *short-term* protective plan. In such cases, what was once helpful now only hurts us, and possibly others as well.

BEYOND THE ACCIDENT STORY

While I had always intended to include dorsal diving in this book, I initially did not plan to write about my father-in-law's accident. After all, it's a pretty personal story. But I ultimately decided to do so for this reason: At the time I was writing this chapter, one of my friends lost a beloved family member. Her family's response was predicably stoic and guarded, just as they had always been throughout her life. But this time, my friend yearned to grieve freely and to be comforted by those who also loved this family member. She additionally wanted to offer her support to anyone who needed it. Yet there was no opening for either scenario, which only intensified my friend's pain.

I know some people might explain others' response (or lack of response) to emotional situations as merely a reflection of their culture or family upbringing. I'm not disputing those connections, and I understand how strong those ties can be. But I also feel compelled to point out that our nervous system works the same wherever we live in this world or whichever family we belong to. So, regardless of what cultural or family norms may have been passed down to us, we are all wired to feel emotions. We are all also wired to comfort others and to be comforted. And when we stray from our biology, we often suffer.

That's why I decided to include the accident story and what transpired afterward. I no longer think that our family's story of unintended painful disconnection is an exception. By sharing our story, I hope it may help others ponder whether they, too, may be dorsal diving and unknowingly hurting those who yearn to connect without guardrails.

I certainly do not want to imply that dorsal divers are the only ones who adversely affect relationships. Hardly—but I've dedicated a large part of this chapter to dorsal diving because I assume that people already know about fight-and-flight behavior, whereas they might not realize that freezing and dissociative behavior are also survival reactions.

To be clear, surging (a fight-or-flight reaction) has its own definite downside.

WHEN SURGING SPIRALS

People are often convinced that surgers act the way they do because it's their *personality*. It must be someone's nature to be so combative, or defensive, or aggressive, or critical, or controlling, or resistant, right? Yet each of those behaviors reflect surging in protection mode.

Chronic fixers—those who continually jump in to solve other people's problems—may be surprised to learn that this reaction is also a form of surging. While chronic fixers can certainly have a true desire to help, their nervous system may not be able to relax until there's a resolution.

People who exhibit recurring flight behavior are also framed in not-so-positive ways. For example, those who frequently delay something, or avoid doing anything different, or back out of decisions at the last minute, or bail as soon as something does not go as imagined are often characterized as untrustworthy, unreliable, and flaky.

But regardless of how we surge, our body will continue to release stress hormones. Consequently, we may end up with too much cortisol in our body—which then becomes problematic. Raised cortisol levels can affect our health, as well as cause insomnia. And what happens when we're not feeling well or getting enough sleep? We're more prone to being irritable and impatient in our relationships.

One protective reaction is not better or worse than another. If we're faced with true danger, all protective-mode reactions are great for the short term. But if we regularly dorsal dive or surge, those reactions will become problematic in our relationships. In such cases, a negative, spiraling effect is almost certain. That's because we'll continue to create a disconnect (whether we realize it or not) with many people.

Perhaps you're not convinced. You might even be thinking, "How do you know those behaviors are reflective of dorsal diving and surging—and not just that person's innate personality or their DNA?" Well, here's what I know. When those very same people are in connection mode, they do not act in any of those disconnecting ways.

WHY WE NEED TO UNDERSTAND OUR NERVOUS SYSTEM

If we remain unaware of how our nervous system works, it will sometimes show up in our life like an unwelcome third party who keeps interfering with our relationships. While that same nervous system is also designed so that we can have incredible connections with others, we may need to help it remember that.

I wish I could say that this chapter completes how our nervous system can mess with us. But recall that our nervous system time-travels with mindboggling speed. It also does not differentiate between what is happening in our mind from what is happening at that present moment.

That's why past events often haunt us in ways that we may not even realize. Before we learn how to return to connection mode, we also need to understand how our past becomes intertwined with our present, which is the focus of the next chapter.

4

~~~~~~~~~

WHEN OUR BRAIN AND NERVOUS SYSTEM HAUNT US

Our brain and nervous system are not intentionally trying to haunt us. And yet at times, it sure can seem that way. But as often is the case, all roads lead back to our biology.

THE FIRST SEVEN YEARS

It turns out that our first seven years of life set the stage for the rest of our life. While that statement might sound like a wildly dramatic claim, our brain functions differently during those formative years. And it's no surprise that this difference has to do with our survival.

It all starts when we make our grand entrance into the world. Even if we are the most adorable baby ever, we know nothing about our new environment. However, we do arrive with an operating system, much like a computer that also has a built-in operating system. But we are more like a computer without any installed software. That's because we don't come with any how-to-survive-in-this-world programs.

Yet we need a way to survive and stay safe in this new, scary place. That's why our brain waves during our first seven years make it super easy to download information from others. Our parents and family members are usually the main sources of such downloads.

That means that *their* software becomes *our* software, just like they received programs from their parents and family members. That means that how we perceive ourselves and the world—whether as a safe or perilous place—comes to us through the lens of other people.

While well intended, this downloading plan has some significant glitches. For starters, this plan does not come with an editor or filter. We download *everything*—the good, the bad, and the ugly—and no one escapes that reality.

HOW IT GETS MESSY

Suppose I had critical parents who regularly used words such as *appropriate* and *inappropriate*, *right* and *wrong*, *proper* and *improper*, and other judgmental words to frame how I acted. First, my parents probably never realized that they likely downloaded those exact words from *their* parents. And it would have been even more improbable that they would have understood that their need to criticize meant that they had already shifted into protection mode.

For example, my parents might fear that I'll never make it in this world if I'm not quiet in public, or if I don't show Emily Post table manners, or if I don't act in the many ways that people deem acceptable. My parents may also fear that others will then judge *them* for not teaching me how to behave "correctly." Of course, any of the above fears is more than enough for a nervous system to sound the alarm.

It's also possible that criticizing has become one of my parents' automated stress reactions. In such case, they are now wired to criticize me (and likely others) as soon as they observe something that they don't believe is acceptable. (If you're having trouble accepting that unsolicited criticism *is* a stress reaction, try withholding such comments for a day. You may be surprised at how that makes you feel.)

But, as a child, I would never have known anything about downloading subconscious programs or how our nervous system sounds that alarm for any perceived threat. However, I did know that I wanted to escape my parents' ongoing criticism. That's why I may have been motivated to do something perfectly—out of *my own fear* of feeling rejection or shame or disappointment if I didn't live up to their standards. Or maybe I already feared that my parents never "saw" me, since I always seemed invisible to them. (Believing I was invisible would have been the "story" that my brain concocted to explain why my parents didn't meet my needs as I hoped.)

But then one day, I did something, and my parents' faces lit up as they said, "You did that perfectly!" Right then, my brain may have thought, "If I am perfect, I will be seen." (The subconscious mind is never logical.) And that's why, somewhere along the way, being a perfectionist became *part of my identity*—even though my penchant for perfectionism keeps me in protection mode.

That is because if I am a perfectionist, I will always have a fear of failing or of being revealed as a fraud. Whether I realize it or not, that never-ending fear is going to influence my daily behavior. Even when my actions create a disconnect with others, my perfectionist program will ensure that I keep acting in the same way.

I may have even convinced myself that my perfectionism is no more than a desire for excellence. I don't consider the possibility that others also revise and redo projects all the time—but they do so with joy and delight as their work improves. They have no fear of the outcome or being judged by their work.

Of course, perfectionism is hardly the only subconscious program that messes with our lives and keeps us in protection mode. Two other programs come to mind that are equally top contenders. For example, people who don't believe they're "good enough" have also downloaded that program.

That subconscious program can start running even at an early age. For example, as a child, we may think that we're not "good enough" if our parents don't offer us much (or any) positive reinforcement, or criticize us whenever we don't meet their expectations, or don't give us the kind of attention that we need. However, from a survival view, we're never going to think that *our parents* are falling short somehow. That would be way too scary. Children need their pack leader to be strong. So the brain goes with the story that we (the child) must not be "good enough." Yet even though we're now adults, we're still running that "I'm not good enough" subconscious program.

Those who identify themselves as people pleasers may also be stuck in protection mode. Although people often think of pleasing and appeasing as having the same meaning, our nervous system views them differently. When we do something to please someone, our action is motivated by joy. But when we do something to *appease* someone, our action is generated by fear. For example, we fear that if we don't say yes, we'll be viewed negatively, or someone will be angry with us if we don't do as expected. So, as a child, we may have gone along with whatever we thought someone wanted to happen just to circumvent that person's anger or disapproval. Or worse, we may have learned that compliance was necessary to escape physical harm.

However, years later as adults, we're still running our "appeasing" subconscious program. While that reaction was likely a necessary survival strategy when we were young, it keeps us in protection mode in our present life. For starters, we often begin to resent being a "people pleaser," since *appeasing* others (again, that's what we're really doing) prevents us from responding authentically and having our own needs met.

Regardless of what subconscious program we are running, our subconscious mind will now actively seek lots of supporting evidence to validate that specific programming. So, in the case of people appeasers, their subconscious mind will keep putting them in situations where they'll feel as though they *have to* say yes or they *have to* comply in some way. Such experiences will then often end with them telling themselves, "See? I told you so!"—as in, "I told you that you'll never get your needs met." After all, that is what they keep experiencing.

Again, this doesn't just happen with people-appeasing subconscious programs. This is how our subconscious mind works for whatever automated programs we are running.

But here's what we may not realize: We continue to have those same experiences only because we keep running our same subconscious programs. And that is how it will continue to go until we delete those disempowering programs and replace them with something else. In other words, we can also run automated programs *that keep us in connection mode.*

TAKING CONTROL

We like to think we're in control of our lives. And yet our subconscious mind leads 95 percent of the time. That fact is even more unsettling once we realize that our subconscious mind is just a bunch of downloaded programs, most of which we acquired at an early age and are now running on autopilot. In other words, there's no one "there" leading most of our life—no wizard hiding behind the curtain (as in *The Wizard of Oz*), no wise sage steering us in the right direction.

But this is not necessarily bad news. That's because most of these subconscious programs are awesome, meaning that we truly need many parts of our life to run on autopilot in order to function. For example, consider how exhausting it would be (and how we would never get anything done) if we had to think—every time—about how to walk, how to tie our shoes, how to drive a car, or how to do anything else that we initially had to learn but now do on autopilot.

If we truly want to take control of our lives, we come to realize that it is a waste of time to blame everyone else for why our life isn't going as we'd like. Instead, we now focus on deleting our disempowering programs and replacing those with more positive, beneficial ones.

Of course, our subconscious mind is never going to quit being in charge. But here's the big difference. Once we change our subconscious's playlist to automate empowering rather than sabotaging programs, our subconscious mind will seek experiences to support that new way of thinking. The same old setup remains—our subconscious programs still dictate 95 percent of our life—only now our subconscious mind is working for us.

HOW WE END UP WITH NO-DATE-STAMP MEMORIES

It's not just disempowering subconscious programs that haunt us. We also experience problematic glitches with how we store certain memories. While the following example is not a true story, it is representative of how our conscious memories do not always tell the whole story.

I'm standing on a corner right next to a rose stand, waiting for the light to turn green. A car is starting to cross the intersection. But suddenly, another driver runs the red light and crashes into that car.

The people in both cars are badly hurt. First responders and ambulances arrive on the scene. Someone has not survived. A small child, who was in the car that ran the red light, is being airlifted to the hospital. The ambulances take away the other people who were hurt.

I am a witness, so I need to stay to talk to the police officers. I'm nauseous and badly shaken. My nervous system needs to release that feeling of sheer dread, helplessness, and fear that I experienced while watching what was unfolding right in front of me.

But I do not know anything about my nervous system. I don't know how to help it process what I just experienced as being over, done—and, most importantly, that I survived. So, while I'm not physically hurt, the accident becomes a memory without a date stamp.

Unfortunately, that means that this experience will keep showing up in my life, even if I do not ever connect what happens in my future with when I was standing on that corner and saw that fatal accident.

THE NEVER-EVER-FORGET-THIS TAG

Memories *without* a date stamp are like photos from a digital camera that are missing the time and date—only when it comes to the brain, that missing date stamp is far more problematic.

First, no-date-stamped memories aren't stored like memories with a coherent beginning, middle, and end, and they don't move on to consolidation and long-term memory storage. Yet they do get a never-ever-forget-this tag.

Once they're tagged that way, our nervous system takes those memories very seriously, as though they're bonded with superglue, always front and center, with a red neon flashing light. After all, we can't forget what happened because *our nervous system still thinks the threat is ongoing.* That's why it remains hypervigilant about anything that is even slightly related to the original threat. Not surprisingly, never-ever-forget-this-tagged memories cause the nervous system to continuously sound the stress alarm.

But here's where the memory gets murky. While I remember

that I was a witness to that accident, I never consciously registered parts of that experience. For example, I didn't realize that I was standing next to roses while I was on that corner. But *a part of my brain* most certainly registered those flowers, as well as how they smelled. My brain also stored the loud sound of the circling helicopters with my feeling of dread as I watched that small child being airlifted. But those details are also not part of my explicit memory of that fatal crash.

However, I *have* noticed that I now start to feel nauseous whenever I'm around roses—and I can't believe my partner just bought me *roses* for my birthday! And years later, I just know that I'm never going on that helicopter tour when my family and I are vacationing in Hawaii, though I can't explain that feeling of dread as soon as I watch them take off.

Of course, these never-ever-forget-this-tagged memories are not restricted to tragic events. We also don't have to even remember the original event for it to influence the rest our life.

For example, suppose a four-year-old overhears her mom telling her dad, "Right now, I'm so angry at my boss, I could kill him!" Now, her husband understands that his wife does not mean that she is about to commit a felony or hire a hitman. But the young daughter takes her mom's comment literally, which is why her brain and nervous system record that conversation like this: Don't ever get Mom angry, or she could kill me.

Because she is four, she will not likely ever have a conscious memory of what she overheard that day. However, her subconscious brain has most certainly recorded this information. And that's why she may now spend the rest of her life appeasing her mother, avoiding her mother, or doing both, since it's far too dangerous to ever risk angering her.

HOW THE BRAIN AND NERVOUS SYSTEM CAN HAUNT VETERANS

It seems incredibly unjust that those who have chosen to defend our country are often the ones who end up with a brain and nervous system that now haunts them. Of course, no one ever intends for that to happen. But it does.

My father was a World War II veteran. But it wasn't until he was 90 years old, nearly 65 years since he was stationed in the Philippines, that he could even begin to talk about his war experiences. Even then, my family and I could feel how much those memories still pained him.

I also have had the honor of getting to know many amazing younger veterans who have found their way to Brain Highways. Each has a story about their deployment and what happened to them after they returned home.

For example, retired Lieutenant Colonel April Wimmer was deployed in Kabul, Afghanistan, when there was an insider shooting. Fifteen of her coworkers were shot. Once home, April had great difficulty sleeping. "I would wake up in the middle of the night, completely panicked, with a full-blown adrenaline rush. I would also go into full-blown panic mode if someone approached my car. My brain was back to the IEDs, even though I was safe and sound at home."

April soon became so hypervigilant that she hated going out in crowds. "The things that once brought me joy, like professional sporting events or a concert, were now a source of great anxiety." She shared how her family was constantly on edge whenever they were around her. That was because they never knew when an encounter would lead to a confrontation or if they would have to leave because she could no longer deal with wherever they were—even if was just a child's birthday party.

Retired Sergeant Major Rusty Baker was also aware that he had changed after returning from his second deployment in Afghanistan.

"I would blow up at home—and you could apologize and say it would never happen again—but it happened again. It would come in such a way that I could not see it coming. It would be over something ridiculous, but I would lose my mind—and for what? This was the family that I fought to protect, that I went overseas to do this for. And now I am home, and they are getting the worst of me." He was also having disturbing thoughts that would not go away.

Of course, those new, alarming changes in behavior did not reflect who April and Rusty were in Afghanistan or, for that matter, who they had been throughout their life. Yet a conglomeration of variables—including *living in a war zone* and all that encompassed—now made it too challenging for them to merely bounce back to civilian life once home.

This is when believing that we have an innate power to change our brain and nervous system, with the knowledge of how to do so, can be such a game-changer. I am very grateful that April, Rusty, and our other Brain Highways veteran participants have now been able to return to civilian life in the ways that they and their families had always imagined. I'm not saying that changing their brain and nervous system were the only reason that these veterans moved forward. But restoring their nervous system's flexibility, which included addressing their lower brain development, was most definitely a significant part of their recovery.

I would also never say that restoring the nervous system's flexibility and finishing the lower brain development are the only ways to help veterans who struggle with post-traumatic stress syndrome (PTSD). I'm equally grateful for all the other people and approaches that help these admirable men and women.

But there are still too many veterans who are struggling. That's why I hope that those men and women will consider how their nervous system and lower brain are presently wired. More times than not, this is where we often find new answers to move us forward.

SCREEN 2

Before my son-in-law became part of our family, I think it was accurate to say that the subconscious mind was not on his list of conversation topics (which is true for most people). And yet one day I found myself trying to explain to him how the subconscious mind greatly influences our life.

I start by giving him the two screens analogy that we refer to in the Brain Highways program. "If we view our life as a movie, then most of us think that our footage is just playing out on only one screen. Yet there is also a Screen 2, where our subconscious programs and those charged, no-date-stamp memories hang out."

I then share some of the ways that Screen 2 often shows up in our life, such as when we engage in self-sabotaging behavior, or the same problem keeps showing up (though possibly in various ways), or we overreact to something others consider mundane, or we resist or avoid something that is helpful. Or we might suspect a Screen 2 connection when we keep having a recurring health problem, especially if it shows up at the same time each year or after a similar situation.

I even tell my future son-in-law how I (unfortunately) predict that many COVID memories are going to end up on people's Screen 2 for the rest of their lives—that is, if people don't go back and get a date stamp on their unresolved experiences. I'm not talking only about those incredibly painful, heart-wrenching times of not being able to be with a loved one who was gravely ill or dying from COVID-19 while in the hospital. I'm also talking about experiences such as when high school seniors had to miss their prom and graduation.

Of course, the conscious mind would argue that not being with a loved one while gravely ill is far worse than missing prom and graduation. But the nervous system and subconscious mind don't see it that way. Any unresolved threat has the potential to show up again and again in our lives until the brain and nervous system get the message that this event is done. Any unfinished COVID experiences (where we haven't felt all the associated emotions so they could pass) are primed to haunt any of us long past the pandemic.

Well, since COVID is on everyone's mind, my future son-in-law does seem somewhat interested as I now explain future possible Screen 2 COVID scenarios.

"The conscious mind would understand the no-visitor COVID rules. But the subconscious mind might be holding on to unexpressed anger toward hospital personnel or have buried anxiety associated with being separated from someone who's ill. Similarly, the conscious mind would have understood why prom and graduation were canceled. But subconsciously, those teens may be holding on to unexpressed resentment toward those in charge, as well as burying sadness for missing both experiences.

That's why, years later, the person who wasn't allowed to be with his loved one may suddenly explode at a young nurse who nicely asks him to step out of the hospital room while running some tests on his son. Or after hearing that a close family member has pneumonia, someone with that same COVID experience may have a full-blown panic attack because she won't be able to care for that family member, since he lives in another state. While distance—and not a hospital rule—is now the reason this person can't be with her loved one, the nervous system sees enough of a similarity to sound the alarm. In the same way, the senior who missed prom and graduation may now be triggered by anything he misses out on for the rest of his life, but his reaction to those future events will seem wildly disproportionate to the actual situation. These are just some of the ways Screen 2 shows up in our life."

Okay, while I'm fully into this topic, I figure I should probably stop. It does cross my mind that my future son-in-law may be just humoring me (as one may feel obligated to do with a future mother-in-law rattling away on a topic), especially since he cannot seem to say "Screen 2" with a straight face.

But awareness can make such a difference.

A few weeks after that discussion on the subconscious mind, we are having dinner with family members, and my future son-in-law is relaying something that happened earlier that day. He's describing a person's over-the-top reaction that didn't seem to match what was happening in real time. And then, with a twinkle in his eye, he looks right at me and says, "Screen 2, right?"

Once we are open to the idea that Screen 2 memories do spill over into our Screen 1 life, we start to see how often this happens. But there are also times when a connection to the past isn't obvious.

For example, some Brain Highways child participants have resisted wearing a seatbelt. For most, their resistant behavior was just one of the many ways they showed being stuck in protection mode.

Yet, in two different cases, it was something more. For these kids, being confined by a seatbelt immediately triggered a never-ever-forget-this-tagged memory of when each of them (in different situations) had been previously pinned down.

Being trapped—and the helplessness that comes with not being able to escape—is a universal primordial fear among all of us. For these kids, the seatbelt triggered an overpowering visceral reaction that was more in line with a confined feral animal trying to escape.

JIM'S BROKEN WRIST (AGAIN)

Recall (from Chapter 3) that Jim broke his wrist when he was 12. And remember that while the break happened during the day, Jim never told his parents that he was in excruciating pain *until midnight*.

If we apply what we now know about subconscious programs, we can first surmise that Jim already had several programs on autopilot back then. That's why he tried to endure the pain all on his own and waited so long to tell his parents what happened. Three subconscious programs come to mind: "Asking for help shows weakness"; "You're on your own"; and "We do not show emotions (other than anger) in this family."

Since Jim's mother still tells the broken wrist story as though it's funny family folklore (there's never a version where she expresses remorse or reflection on why her son didn't reach out to her until hours and hours later), we can also assume that Jim didn't get a date stamp on that episode. Also, knowing that dorsal diving was modeled as the norm in his home, it equally follows that Jim did a dorsal dive to dissociate from the emotional pain of believing that he had to endure the experience all on his own. The fact that his mom still laughs whenever she tells the story lends credence to those conclusions.

But Jim's broken wrist at 12 is also an example of how the subconscious mind seeks to create experiences that reinforce our downloaded programs. Most often, those kinds of confirming experiences are only similar to what previously happened rather than exact replications of the prior experiences.

Yet, in Jim's case, since he first broke his wrist at age 12, he has now broken that same wrist three more times.

The second time Jim breaks his wrist, he's coaching our eight-year-old's softball team, and he's showing the players how to slide into second base. But as soon as Jim does that, it's apparent to everyone that he has done something to his wrist—and that he's in a lot of pain. Yet Jim insists that his wrist is not broken—that it's maybe only sprained. He refuses to go to the emergency room or see a doctor even when it's still throbbing days later.

The third time Jim breaks his wrist, he's out on a run (by himself) during his lunch break from work, which is about 40 minutes from our home. This time, he trips on a crack in the road and falls. He's pretty sure that he has broken that same wrist.

But what does he do? He hitchhikes a ride back to his work. Once there, he doesn't tell anyone; instead, he gets in his car and drives himself to urgent care. A doctor confirms the break and puts a compression cast on him. He goes back to work, as though he has just been out on an errand.

The fourth time Jim breaks his wrist, he is also running. It's early morning, and he is out on a trail relatively near our house. Again, he trips—but this time on a rock. He uses that same arm to brace his fall as he crashes to the ground.

Jim immediately calls to tell me what has happened. I, of course, say that I will come right away. As I am driving, I'm thinking about how I can convince him to go to an urgent care facility, even though prior experiences suggest that he will shut down the idea.

But to my surprise, Jim says that I need to drive him straight to the emergency room. Even the part about having *me* be the one who drives is shockingly out of character.

Once at the hospital, we learn that Jim has broken that same wrist in multiple places. The breaks are so bad that he ends up needing surgery that requires a plate and screws to hold the bones together to help them heal.

As a side (but relevant) note, when the orthopedic surgeon was examining the X-rays for Jim's current broken wrist, he pointed to an area near the new break and said, "What is that? It looks like a broken bone that didn't heal as it is supposed to." That area was exactly where Jim claimed he had only "sprained" his wrist when he slid into second base.

Sure, anyone might frame Jim's *four* broken wrists as nothing more than that accidents will happen—and leave it at that. But that would be glossing over something important, especially when we understand our subconscious programming.

After his fourth break, *Jim did not hesitate to reach out and ask for help.* So why the radical change after the fourth break? Well, between breaks three and four, Jim had spent time doing some nervous system repair work, which included exploring which of his disempowering programs were running on autopilot. As implausible as that might seem, that prior work might have opened the door for a different ending with broken wrist number four.

I say that because even after Jim's trip to the emergency room and subsequent surgery, he continued to allow our daughters and me to take care of him while he healed. And while admittedly asking for help is still not always Jim's first go-to thought, he has continued to do so, such as when he asked his son-in-law to help him move a heavy table. Before, he would have moved that table all by himself, even knowing it would have hurt his back for days.

Of course, time will tell whether Jim is done breaking that wrist. But since his original subconscious program (asking for help is a sign of weakness) has clearly been updated, we can hope that his subconscious mind is no longer seeking experiences to confirm that Jim must endure everything by himself.

When it comes to our subconscious mind, this will never change: We will always run our automated programs for 95 percent of our life. However, we *can* change which programs it plays.

So if we want to change our life, we change our programs.

TIME FOR CONNECTION MODE

In this chapter, as well as in Chapters 1–3, you learned how the nervous system tries to protect us whenever it thinks there's a threat. But just as we are innately wired for survival, a part of our nervous system is also wired for connection. When that circuitry is activated, we call it being in connection mode, the focus of the next chapter.

5

~~~~~~~~~

THE PATH TO
CONNECTION MODE

A t the start of Brain Highways, the words *connection mode* were never even on our radar.

Instead, this was our original game plan: Get out of survival mode (the lower centers of the brain) and return to the cortex (the higher centers of the brain). That's because once there, we can be rational, coherent, and analytical, and when we are demonstrating these qualities, we appear calm and grounded. So back then, being "in the cortex" seemed like the obvious endgame.

That is, until we could make the case that being in our cortex was sometimes just survival mode in disguise. For example, maybe our voice did sound calm. But were we really in our cortex if we were trying to persuade others that they were wrong and we were right? Or maybe we did appear grounded. But were we really in our cortex if we were doubling down with facts until others saw the same logic and rationale as we did?

More and more, the general description of being in our cortex did not always seem to be the opposite of being in survival mode.

IF NOT THE CORTEX?

Full disclosure: It wasn't like I was observing only how *other people* could disconnect while being "in their cortex." I now put myself at the top of that list.

Sure, I could easily rattle off logical, sensible reasons why I was right about something in a calm, matter-of-fact voice. But there was also that part of me that just *had to* follow Jim into another room as I continued to make my case. It gets worse. Knowing that Jim was a captive audience when showering, I would even sometimes stand outside the shower door to prove my point. (In retrospect, I'm sure that the loud, running shower water just made it easier for him to tune me out.)

It finally became obvious. My penchant for following Jim around the house while hammering away with my "rational" thinking— even holding him hostage to get him to agree with me—was clearly a disguised form of surging. Forget that I was calmly presenting my case. Why did I need to be right? More importantly, what did I fear might happen if he did not share my view?

I was now convinced that protection-mode behaviors were not limited to the obvious, such as yelling, getting defensive, and throwing objects. At times, any of us could (unknowingly) masquerade as being in our cortex—when we were, in fact, in protection mode. But since I previously believed that being in the cortex was the ultimate goal, now what?

Around that same time, I had someone in my life who, I admit, bugged me, but I could not figure out why. In fact, others seemed to view this man in a positive light. I would even say that most resonated with his predictable, matter-of-fact approach to everything.

Yet my not-so-positive reaction to him continued. I finally did a rhetorical exercise that has helped me in the past (though I cannot recall where I first learned this): I asked, "If I could give [name of person] some advice, what would that be?" Since I had already done this exercise at other times, I knew that my answer for this man would somehow be applicable *to me*, which is the whole point of asking the question.

Well, right away, I knew my answer. My advice to this man was, "Hey, how about showing some heart?"

And right then, I knew how that advice applied to me as well. At times, I, too, could certainly intellectualize a situation, stick to the facts, and do a thorough analysis when interacting with others— *while parking my heart elsewhere*. Ouch.

With that eye-opener, I now challenged myself to show more heart in my daily interactions. Rather quickly, I was surprised at how my connections with others were all-around better. And that's when I started pondering: How might I also include the heart as part of the Brain Highways program?

ENTER THE HEART

While I had now become enthused about the heart, I had a problem. Brain Highways was a *brain* program.

So I started slowly. First, I only shared the ways that people had already commonly talked about the heart in everyday conversations. For example, we had all heard people say: "He had a change of heart." "She poured her heart out." "He is so young at heart."

And then there were the ways that people talked about the heart when giving advice, such as: "Follow your heart." "Listen to your heart." Or the way people inadvertently referred to the heart's innate wisdom when they said something like "In my heart, I already knew what I was going to do."

From there, we shared with our Brain Highways participants that the survival brain and heart did not send the same kind of messages. For example, even our youngest participants understood that their heart would never tell them to "grab the iPad out of your brother's hand because he's never going to share it with you."

But a heart message could also contradict a cortex-only message.

That's why we also provided examples of when such messages might conflict, such as:

- "The heart tells me when it is time to let go (of whatever) so I can move on, even though the cortex is still focused on why I should double down on my position."

- "The heart tells me to show up somewhere, even though my cortex does not understand why (at least at that moment)."

- "The heart tells me to slow down, even though the cortex is listing all the reasons I cannot rest."

Fortunately, our participants seemed intrigued with what we were starting to share about the heart. But I still felt as though I had to tiptoe around this new component.

THE INCREDIBLE FACTS

As often is the case with Brain Highways (meaning that I do not recall how this happened), I eventually came across a nonprofit organization called the HeartMath Institute. This was before the HeartMath Institute became the global forerunner that it is today. However, I was over the moon to discover that the founders had already done lots of research on what they called "heart-brain coherence." That meant there were already proven *facts* about the heart, which made a most compelling case to now include "leading with the heart" in our program. Here's some of what I learned from the HeartMath Institute:

- In 1994, scientists discovered about 40,000 brain-like cells in the heart, called sensory neurites.

- This means that the heart is a sensory organ, as well as an information encoding and processing center.

- The heart has its own nervous system that enables it to learn, remember, and make decisions independent of the brain.

- The heart is in continuous communication with the brain and body through multiple pathways.

- The conversation between the heart and brain is important. The emotional signals that our heart sends to our brain then dictate what kind of chemicals our brain releases in response.

- While the heart and brain communicate with each other, the heart sends more information to the brain than the brain does to the heart.

That last fact—that the *heart* sends more information to the brain than the brain does to the heart—seemed to solidify the importance of including the heart as part of changing our brain. To exclude it would be like keeping an MVP out of the game.

The HeartMath Institute also focused on something called the heart variability rate (HVR). They emphasized that this was not the same as the heart rate, which is how many times the heart beats per minute. Instead, the HVR is the naturally occurring variations in the time between heartbeats—which then results in specific heart rhythms and patterns. The brain then relies on these rhythms and patterns to decide what kind of chemicals and hormones to release in response.

For example, when we feel emotions such as gratitude, appreciation, and compassion, we show a coherent heart rhythm pattern. When the brain picks up on these signals, it releases oxytocin (which has rightly earned the "feel-good" hormone nickname). In contrast, when we feel emotions such as fear, anger, and frustration, we show an incoherent heart rhythm pattern. When the brain picks up on these signals, it releases adrenaline and other stress hormones.

Of course, bringing the heart on board at Brain Highways didn't mean that we were now ditching the cortex. After all, the heart needed to work with the cortex since it was up to the cortex to execute the heart's messages.

THE FULL JOURNEY

With our new merger, the cortex was no longer exercising its prior automatic veto power over messages from the heart. Instead, the cortex and heart now worked together as formidable partners.

For example, suppose we hear our heart say, "Go for it." But then our cortex reminds us that we don't have the money or skills or time to do whatever our heart is urging us to act on. However, we now no longer conclude that the heart's message must be wrong. Instead, we appreciate the cortex's reminder that, yes, we will need to explore creative ways (and we *are* the most creative when the heart and cortex are working together) to address whatever details may be a temporary roadblock to following our heart. But instead of viewing the cortex and heart as adversaries, we now view them as working together on the same team.

While we didn't initially realize it, we had moved the goalposts. It was no longer enough to get out of protection mode and back to the cortex. In the new endgame, we wanted to be running our heart-to-cortex circuitry as much as possible.

And there it was, right in front of us. Being in the cortex was *not* the opposite of being in protection mode. The opposite of being in protection mode was (drumroll, please) being in connection mode—or as we were now otherwise referring to this heart-to-cortex circuitry, running the "gold."

We also realized that the journey to the heart brought us back to when we arrived in this world. From the moment we took our first breath, we were wired and ready to connect. No one had to teach us to intuitively turn to our mother or feel safe in her arms.

As babies, we then naturally and gleefully responded to people's loving tone and smiling faces, which only encouraged such people to connect with us even more.

We *are* all wired to connect. But if we've been stuck in protection mode for a long time, we may have forgotten that biological truth.

ONCE IN CONNECTION MODE

At the start of the Brain Highways program, participants write what they hope will change in their lives. They commonly write about challenges with one or more of the following areas: anxiety, focus, learning, speech, social interactions, sensory processing, sleep, memory, motor skills, emotional regulation, transitions, depression, coordination, and organization. To date, no one has written, "I hope to spend more time in connection mode."

Their specific answers, though, are hardly a surprise. After all, the world's prime-time message screams at us to "fix" a specific problem or even "fix" the person who has become problematic.

And yet this is what happens when participants share their changes at the end of the course. Yes, they will quickly note how learning has become joyful, or how they are sleeping better, or how they can now easily articulate their thoughts, or how any of the other challenges they previously listed have greatly improved or are no longer even a struggle. But what do they really want to talk about? Their new life in connection mode—and how that has made every part of their life so much easier.

Initially, I hesitated to include examples of what these participants shared. I didn't want to sound like some tacky infomercial. (Hang out in connection mode—and live the life of your dreams!) However, since I give a lot of airtime to life in protection mode (four chapters), it seems remiss not to also give you a glimpse of life in connection mode.

There's another important reason that I want to share some connection-mode stories. It's not like others haven't encouraged (and
even told) us to be more confident, compassionate, creative, curious,
calm, decisive, and trustworthy—as though we can just *will* those
traits at whim. But most of us have yet to understand that these
admirable qualities are the *by-products* of living a life in connection
mode. We don't adopt these characteristics to get to connection
mode. We acquire these traits by already being there. In truth, everything incredible only happens *after we are in connection mode*. I hope
the following connection-mode examples and stories help convince
you of that truth.

CONFIDENCE AND DECISION-MAKING

Before I learned any of the information in this book, my family
and I did not understand why my oldest sister, Marcia, found it
challenging to make even the smallest decision. So we didn't ask
her to do anything that required a decision. Or we would assign her
something simple. For Thanksgiving, we might say, "Just bring some
rolls from a bakery."

Yet we'd still get so many calls. For example, the first call would
often come an hour later. "But what kind of rolls?" The next day,
"Do I need to pick them up *on* Thanksgiving?" The following day,
"If I get the rolls the day before Thanksgiving, will they still be
fresh enough?"

Not only could Marcia not make simple decisions, but I later
came to understand another part of her predictable, endless questions. People who ask lots of questions do so because one of their
automated stress reactions is to seek reassurance. Since they fear they
will make the "wrong" decision, they need reassurance that will help
them get it "right"—that is, until the fear returns (which it always
does) and they now ask yet another question.

But once I began leading with my heart, I started to frame Marcia's inability to make decisions more compassionately. I thought about her type 1 diabetes, which is often erratic and sometimes causes her blood sugar to go dangerously high. So not only did Marcia need to be cognizant about what she ate, but she also needed to *decide* how to adjust her insulin accordingly.

Well, Marcia's daily insulin challenges, *combined with how her brain and nervous system were wired at that time*, kept her in protection mode and at her threshold. Consequently, her brain and nervous system were exhausted from focusing on her diabetes and keeping her alive. That's why something as mundane as Thanksgiving rolls was never going to rate as even remotely important.

When Marcia was nearly 60, she finally decided to do the Brain Highways program. However, apart from that decision, Marcia still lived alone. Family members and friends had a justifiable concern that her blood sugar might suddenly shoot up dangerously high, causing her to end up in a coma. And that's when Marcia learned about diabetic alert dogs that (amazingly!) are trained to detect blood sugar levels.

However, here was the gotcha. Getting one of these special dogs required lots and lots of decisions, such as choosing a program, paying a (significant) financial investment up front, making all the flight and hotel arrangements (since no training sites were anywhere near her home), figuring out how to get from her hotel to the training center each day to do the two-week training, and more.

But with her new highways in place, Marcia now made all those decisions! And then, the following happened during her first night at the hotel.

Her assigned dog, Laurene, has already been brought to her room. Laurene is supposed to sleep by Marcia's bed. In the morning, they will both go to the site to start the official training.

It's getting late—it is already close to 11:00, so Marcia goes to sleep. But at 2:00 a.m., she wakes up because Laurene has jumped onto the bed and is relentlessly licking and pawing her. At first, Marcia is confused. But then it dawns on her to look at her insulin pump—only to see that it reads, *"Pump failed"* at 11:08 p.m.! That means Marcia had not received any insulin in nearly three hours!

Four hours and multiple insulin injections later, Marcia's blood sugar now reads 388—which is still considered much higher than it should be. But she also understands that her blood sugar must have been dangerously high at the time Laurene awakened her. She could have lapsed into a coma or maybe even died.

Years later, Marcia will not hesitate to tell you, "Laurene is one of the best decisions I've ever made in my life." (The extra sweet part of that proclamation is the way Marcia now frames herself as someone who makes decisions.)

That initial decision had an amazing ripple effect. Laurene's heroic response in that hotel room ended up being chosen as one of the stories for the Chicken Soup for the Soul book *My Hilarious, Heroic, Human Dog.* All royalties from that book go to American Humane, an organization that has been promoting the welfare and safety of animals for more than 100 years. Laurene and Marcia's story was even picked to be one of the few featured from that book on Chicken Soup for the Soul's podcast.

So if we create a timeline here, this sequence of events began when Marcia first decided to change her brain and nervous system. That then made it possible for her to spend much more time in connection mode. As a by-product of that shift, Marcia then had the *confidence* to make all those decisions to get Laurene. That decision not only maybe saved her life but also ended up being a story in a publication whose proceeds help animals in need of rescue, shelter, protection, and security.

I'd say that's a far cry from when Marcia struggled to bring rolls to Thanksgiving. This story also reflects how much good just seems to happen naturally—once we start living more of our life in connection mode.

When our participants make that shift, they, too, discover a new confidence that changes their life. For example, many of our participants were too afraid to leave their home when they first started Brain Highways. These participants would share that they had always felt some angst—though their anxiety had not previously interfered with much of their overall life. But at one point, their fears escalated to the point where they no longer felt safe to venture outside their home. And so now their anxiety *was* dominating everything.

For those kids who were homebound, their prior anxiety had intensified over time, so that they now refused to go to places such as school, dance class, or soccer practice. For adults, that meant they no longer went to the movies, restaurants, and church. No amount of verbal encouragement could sway these kids and adults to get back into the world. Sure, they still felt angst at home, but it felt safer there than in the outside, scary world.

But they *could* do the Brain Highways program in their home, without ever stepping outside. And so their nervous system and brain began to change. Best of all, these kids and adults understood that *they* were the ones bringing about such changes. They also acquired a myriad of calming actions, along with firsthand experiences of bouncing back to connection mode. At one point, these kids and adults now decided to venture back into the world. No, the world had not changed—but they had. They were now going out in the world with a different brain and nervous system.

And that's why at the end of the Brain Highways course, these kids also gleefully share that they've just spent the night at a friend's house (first time ever!) or how they are going to get on a plane (by themselves!) to visit their grandmother. The adults, too, beam as they share how much of their prior life they have now resumed.

Other participants with never-ending angst (although their level of anxiety had not rendered them homebound) also happily share the many ways their new confidence is showing up in their life. For example, such kids were now trying out for a sports team, or auditioning for a part in a play, or seeking a leadership position at their school. Their visits to the dentist and doctor, which had previously produced much anxiety (and often violent reactions), were now no different from the way most of us experience such appointments. (No one loves having dental work done, but we go without it being an ordeal.) Adults with prior never-ending angst share that they were now offering their opinion at work, considering a new job, going on a trip to somewhere they had always wanted to go, and more.

While the specifics of what participants share will vary, there is always this general theme. This new, natural decision-making and confidence only started happening *after* these adults and kids began spending more and more time in connection mode.

PEACE, CALM, AND COMPASSION

Somewhere along the path to connection mode, participants start to experience a surprising visceral feeling of peace. Even their body language and facial expressions visibly change, reflective of their new calmness. In fact, one participant shared that she had to keep telling people, "No, I did *not* have a facelift."

Another participant shared, "The biggest change for me was finding peace. But I also know now when there is not peace, the *possibility* of peace is always present." That last simple statement reflects a true understanding of the way our nervous system works. No, we cannot always guarantee that we will feel peaceful. But when we have experienced returning to connection mode, we also know that we will feel peaceful again.

Once participants start feeling peaceful, their daily decisions reflect how they're now more relaxed than tense. For example, a parent in the family program shared, "Since I've been feeling so calm these days, I no longer think that I *have to* do another load of laundry right at that moment. Instead, I'll get down on the floor and build a block tower with my kids."

The adults also often express sheer delight over how they are now being playful and lighthearted, no longer acting as though everything in life needs to be so serious. The kids, on the other hand, commonly characterize feeling more peaceful with a short sentence, such as "I just feel calm now," or "I don't get so upset anymore," or "I can go with the flow."

Compassion is also a by-product of time in connection mode. For example, Jack's mom shared this story about her son during one of our classes.

> It's after school, and Jack walks up to his first-grade teacher (from the previous year) to say hello. But she's standing next to one of her students who's clearly upset and on the verge of tears. He's worried that his nanny isn't going to show up, especially since the rest of the kids in his class have already gone home. Nothing the teacher is saying is consoling him.
>
> So Jack turns to the first grader and says, "Okay, I can help you feel better." And then, Jack starts modeling many of the techniques he has already experienced calm his body. Well, the first grader follows Jack's lead, and rather quickly, I see the first grader start to relax. He even smiles!
>
> All along, Jack is so nonchalant, as though this kind of incredible display of kindness and compassion—and this amazing connection that he's making with a kid he doesn't even know—is so commonplace. This is not the Jack I've known for the last seven years of his life. I was completely blown away!

While Jack's mother was amazed by her son's display of compassion, that is what happens naturally in connection mode. Since we're no longer solely focused on our own survival, we are attuned to what others may need. Being in connection mode now makes it possible *to be present* to help others "survive" whatever has put them in protection mode.

PHYSICAL AND MENTAL HEALTH SURPRISES

Participants also share miraculous stories related to their long-term physical health problems. They'll exclaim how a prior condition has either greatly improved or, sometimes, even disappeared altogether.

When I first started hearing these stories, I had no reason to think that these participants were not being truthful. But I confess that some of these changes seemed almost unbelievable.

For example, a participant claimed that she no longer had restless leg syndrome after 20 years of living with this condition. Another participant shared that after going to every specialist for his relentless sciatica nerve pain, it was now gone. We even had two kids (in different sessions) whose poor eyesight resulted in a legally blind diagnosis. Yet both kids' eye doctors were blown away by how much their eyesight had improved after their participation in the program. One, a teenager, was ecstatic when she was told she could now get her driver's license!

Of course, I would always smile whenever such participants excitedly shared their dramatic physical health changes—even though I was thinking, "How is that possible?" But as I learned more about the nervous system, I started to understand.

Once we have shifted into protection mode, our body is solely focused on the imminent threat, and so all healing is automatically put on the back burner. From a survival view, that makes total sense. After all, our sciatic nerve pain is inconsequential if a mountain lion is about to eat us for lunch.

The problem, though, is that the nervous system "sees" mountain lions—like, all the time—in our daily, mundane life. So once

Brain Highways participants started encountering fewer and fewer mountain lions in their day (meaning they were spending more time in connection mode), their body now had a chance to focus on healing.

Participants with eating disorders or addictions will also claim that their recovery seems so much easier "this time around." What is different now? Well, they are in recovery with a different brain and nervous system. They are in recovery while spending more and more time in connection mode. Of course, changing the brain and nervous system are never intended to replace professional help or traditional treatment plans. But landing in connection mode can greatly enhance people getting their lives back on track.

THE RETURN OF EMOTIONS

Some of our participants are caught by surprise when they "suddenly" start experiencing emotions. This even happens to people who have professed themselves as those who "do not do emotions," although it's more accurate to say that they don't *show* emotions.

Such was the case when one of the dads in our family program wanted to tell me what had recently happened to him.

> Hey, Nancy, *what* is going on here? I haven't cried in like four decades. But yesterday, as I am listening to the radio while driving along the road, a song comes on that reminds me of my mom.
>
> And next thing I know, I am *crying*. I'm like, "Seriously? Considering everything that has happened to me in my life, *this* is when I cry?"

But recall that expert dorsal divers have spent much of their life burying their feelings. So as strange as it may sound, the nervous system needs to first believe that it's safe to feel. Even more importantly, we need to have the confidence that we can experience intense emotions *and* still return to connection mode.

As an analogy, suppose I told you to jump off a cliff into the ocean—but you have no way of knowing that you will not keep going down, down into the sea without ever coming back up for air. Are you going to make that jump? Absolutely not. Well, the nervous system has the same answer if it believes that there is no coming back from feeling that emotional pain. So by the time these Brain Highways participants started crying, they had already experienced returning to connection mode many times. Their "sudden" tears could be viewed as feeling it was now safe to allow those buried emotions to surface.

SO NOW WHAT?

By now, I hope you are thinking, "Great! Lead me to connection mode!"

But I will also understand if some of you are thinking, "Sounds too good to be true. After all, how can so many problems be solved by landing in connection mode?" I get that view, especially since traditional approaches focus on trying to solve each specific problem, one by one.

Or you may be thinking, "Okay, I do believe that spending time in connection mode helped those people. But you don't know *my* child's history (or my own). Some changes are just not possible for my child (or me)."

Over the years, many of our participants share those exact thoughts when they start our course. I then ask if they would like me to respond based on our years of experience with how the brain and nervous system work. They always say yes. (I think, subconsciously, they're hoping that I will say that they're wrong.)

However, I first agree with them. I say, "If you think that an easier life is not possible for your child or you, then you are right. That's because our brain believes whatever we think and then works overtime to ensure that our thoughts become our reality." I am not being dismissive when I say that. I am simply relaying how the brain works.

But I also want them to know this often-forgotten truth about our biology: Every single person on this planet is wired for connection mode because *connecting with others is a significant part of our nervous system.* Yes, part of our nervous system works round-the-clock to keep us safe and is laser-focused on our survival. But the other part of our nervous system—when we activate our heart-to-cortex highways—is every much a part of our biology as our survival circuitry. Yet it's very possible that these parts of our nervous system aren't currently working with each other as intended.

This second answer leaves the door open for the possibility of change *under new and different circumstances.* Fortunately, our brain doesn't have to be fully convinced of something before we move forward. Being curious is good enough.

You, too, only need to be curious at this point.

THE GATEWAY TO CONNECTION MODE

Recall that we cannot change how our survival nervous system works. It is always going to make risk assessments before our conscious mind comes on board. It is always going to choose whether we respond with a flight, fight, freeze, or dissociative reaction with no input whatsoever from our conscious mind. However, none of that is a problem *if we have a flexible nervous system.* Flexible here means that we can easily bounce back to connection mode after shifting into protection mode. That is why (long drumroll) *a flexible nervous system is the gateway to connection mode.*

That flexibility is what then allows both parts of our nervous system to work as intended. With such flexibility, we now reap all the benefits of our entire nervous system: The survival part keeps us safe; the connection part allows us to shine.

However, there's a glitch in this system. If (for whatever reason) we're not easily bouncing back to connection mode or we're not bouncing back at all, our nervous system loses its original flexibility. That's how we end up with an inflexible and rigid nervous system primed to keep us in protection mode.

In such cases, we need to *restore* our nervous system's innate flexibility. *Restore* is also a key word here. When we restore something, we return it to its original condition. That means we're never starting from scratch. Like I said, we're already wired for a flexible nervous system.

And that's why the rest of this book presents exactly how we go about restoring our nervous system's flexibility, along with many specific actions that get you started moving in this direction right away. (There are no cliff-hangers in this book. I'm not going to tease you with how great connection mode is and then not share with you how to land there.)

So in Part 3, you'll learn how to resolve false alarms *in real time*, since our nervous system's assessment of true danger is almost always wrong. Resolving perceived threats means doing visceral actions to quickly convince your nervous system and brain that you *are safe* (so no need to keep sounding the alarm). You'll also learn what replenishes your nervous system and why you'd want to do such actions daily. And as you go down this path, you'll likely discover that some or much of your nervous system's current landscape is rocky terrain. If so, you'll learn how to clear and repair those areas. Doing all the above—not just parts of this process—is what restores your nervous system's flexibility. No, it's not a fast process, but it's absolutely doable.

A MISSING PIECE OF THE PUZZLE

In the first part of this book, I lay the groundwork for understanding why a flexible nervous system is key to an easier life. Here, I give you the heads-up that the third part presents the specifics for restoring your nervous system's flexibility.

So then, what is the second part of this book about? Well, it focuses on a common variable that greatly affects whether we even end up with a flexible nervous system. Most importantly, this component is not something included in other traditional nervous system approaches.

Part 2 is all about the lower brain connection. When it comes to restoring the nervous system's flexibility, the lower brain information is so important that it can't fit on a single page in the repairing chapter in the third part of this book. This component is even too big to be its own separate chapter.

The lower brain connection needs its own part. That way, you can understand why approaches that don't include the lower brain may not yield the same kind of lasting results. You can discover why incomplete lower brain development causes so much ongoing stress in people's lives—and even more so when people do not know about this connection.

Once you're at that point in Part 2, you'll want to know how to complete the lower brain development (if you're now thinking that yours or someone else's is incomplete), as well as what you can do in the meantime to make life easier. All this information also appears in the second part of this book.

In a way, placing the lower brain section between the first and third sections is a metaphor. Here, the lower brain information becomes the bridge between acquiring knowledge of the nervous system (the first section) and how to restore its flexibility (the third section).

While you may be tempted to leap over this bridge and go straight to Part 3 (I want to experience changes right now!), I hope you will take the time to walk across this bridge. Here's why: Many people have not completed their lower brain development. That is why you'll likely think of people you know (or you may even "see" yourself) as you learn about a possible lower brain connection. Most importantly, a lower brain connection is often the missing puzzle piece for those who continue to struggle with little or no signs of improvement. That's why learning about a possible lower brain connection is next on the path to a flexible nervous system—and the sole focus of Part 2.

PART 2

The Lower Brain Connection: An Unexpected Possibility

6

HOW THE LOWER BRAIN
CAME INTO THE STORY

ong before I understood the importance of a flexible nervous
system, I was focused on the lower brain connection. But, in
truth, I never planned to learn about the lower brain. It's a
rather wild story the way everything just happened. For starters, this
is a mystery story, complete with foreshadowing, a trail of baffling
clues, and yours truly playing the role of detective.

Since the brain enjoys a good mystery, I've decided to unfold this
story to you in the exact way that I experienced it. That means you
will learn the answers at the same point they were revealed to me. I
can assure you that, like all good mysteries, this one is solved by the
end of the story.

I do have another reason for introducing you to this important topic via this true story. It's possible that you've been thinking,
"Wait—if the lower brain development is such an important part
of repairing our nervous system and for experiencing an easier life,

then why haven't I heard about this before?" It's a fair question. As of now, the lower brain connection has certainly not made it to prime time. However, not knowing about the lower brain connection does not negate its importance or validity.

Still, if a nervous system assesses this new knowledge as a threat to someone's personal narrative or professional training, it will not hesitate to sound the alarm. So I only want you to become aware of this lower brain connection. What you end up doing with this information is always up to you. For now, you're just reading what happened to other people in this true story.

That way, your brain has a chance to process certain facts that lend credibility to the existence of a lower brain connection, such as that this story began in the public schools—an institution hardly known for being ahead of its time. Initial funding came from a well-established bank that has been around since 1852. Banks, too, are not known for being innovative, let alone reckless with their money. This story spans two decades; the lower brain connection isn't some temporary trend. It has upheld the test of time.

And so I share this uncanny story of how I happened to stumble on the lower brain connection.

THE VERY BEGINNING

In 1999, I was an educational writing consultant at different public schools in affluent neighborhoods. These schools weren't like the one that I had taught at in the '80s—where the parents of my students were often heroin addicts, or my students lived with 20 people in a small rundown apartment. These students had easy access to many enrichment programs, tutoring, and more. And yet so many of them were struggling to learn. I could not shake a recurring thought: Are we missing something?

That thought would not go away. I ended up proposing a plan

to the principal at Paul Ecke Central, an elementary school in Encinitas, California (one of the schools where I was the writing consultant). I wanted to try and discover which piece of the puzzle we were missing. The local Wells Fargo bank graciously agreed to fund my proposal, which was rather remarkable since my original plan was scarce on details.

Basically, I was going to teach the same group of 16 fourth graders for the second half of each school day. The 16 were selected because they had already been identified as "at risk" since they were reading at a kindergarten or first-grade level. Most of the group also demonstrated disruptive classroom behavior.

It's the first day, and we're meeting in the small classroom connected to the school's media center. Instead of desks, there are tables in the room. Yet that doesn't concern me—that is, until the kids come inside and sit down.

Once the kids are seated at those tables, it's clear that they have no innate sense of spatial boundaries. They lean on or elbow one another. One of the students even pushes the student sitting next to him. I make a quick decision. I tell everyone to come to the front of the room and sit on the carpet.

Well, I'm not prepared for the ensuing stampede. It seems more like wild antelope than elementary students charging toward me. I keep motioning for them to stay back, but they seem clueless about leaving any space between them and me. For a moment, I have visions of being trampled, leaving behind a mere imprint of my body on the carpet.

But they finally settle, only to start leaning on and shoving one another all over again. The concept of space boundaries is clearly nonexistent to this group.

The next day, I act on a hunch. I ask the custodian to bring more tables into our already small classroom. But the extra tables now allow me to extend each student's work area by almost doubling the space between one student and the next. It works like magic— no one is invading another person's space!

Clearly, if these students' true intent was to lean on, elbow, or push someone else, then any of the 16 (I'd come to fondly think of my students as simply "the 16") could have easily risen from their chair and moved toward another student. But none of them ever did that. However, I still didn't understand why simply expanding their work area boundaries was so effective in helping them stay in their own space.

Over the next several weeks, I noticed how this group shared many other unusual behaviors. For example, the 16 touched everything in sight. It was as though an invisible magnet pulled them to whatever they saw until they were close enough to grab it. Seconds later, I would often watch them drop whatever they had just picked up—and yes, that object would sometimes break. But I never sensed that they were intentionally trying to destroy these items.

The 16 were also inclined to chew on nearly everything—pencils, hood strings, paper, shirts, hair, and more, especially whenever they were concentrating or feeling anxious. There was more. If I stood directly in front of them whenever I asked a question, they answered. But if their backs were to me, it was as though I was asking the question to the wind. They didn't even seem to know I was there.

And then there were those mysterious behaviors when it came to academics. For example, the 16 might recognize a simple three-letter word when reading it aloud, but then moments later, they would write that same word differently (and they had no clue they had done that). In general, their inventive spelling was challenging for even the most seasoned teacher to decipher. The first letter of a word was often all that was correct; sometimes that wasn't even the case.

There was also their undeniable aversion to copying any information from the whiteboard.

But from the beginning, one behavior was the most obvious. The 16 needed to move—like, all the time. If they could move while engaging in a task, they could pay attention. If they were sitting still, they could not focus. This realization coincided with a reassignment to a larger classroom. That bigger space now gave me the opportunity to try some ideas I'd been pondering.

In this new classroom, I had the 16 do movements such as jump on a mini-trampoline while spelling words, walk across a balance beam while reading sight words, and bounce a basketball as many times as the answer to addition and subtraction problems. Every 15 minutes, they rotated to a new station to engage in different kinds of movement while learning. This format made an indisputable difference in their ability to stay on task.

Of course, I still didn't understand why the 16 acted the way they did. Yet by now, I was 100 percent certain that they all wanted to learn, and that they *could* learn—as long as I kept making many modifications for them.

A FEW ANSWERS

Recall that this was 1999, so internet search engines were still new to the masses. While it's hard to imagine today, this was before large numbers of people could easily access online information from their home. But with my s-l-o-w, dial-up computer (some readers may not even know what I am talking about), I started to explore. I was looking for something on the world wide web that might tie together the 16's unique behaviors.

My first aha moment came when I discovered something called the vestibular and proprioceptive sensory systems. Initially, I thought, "What? There are more than the five senses we've all been taught?" Then I learned that there were some very specific move-ments to help these (new-to-me) sensory systems.

That information changed how the 16 moved during class. I now had them do *those* movements to wake up what appeared to be their sluggish vestibular and proprioceptive systems. No question, that change made it even easier for them to focus. However, such effects were only short term. It was like they continually needed to do those movements—or they were back to square one, where they, once again, could not stay on task.

Still, the principal at this school was impressed with how the 16 were improving academically, which is why he asked me to do a training for the teachers. Instead, I suggested that we have the 16 do the presentation, which would allow them to share how they were able to learn in this new and different way.

And that's what happened.

The training begins with more than just the Paul Ecke Central teachers in the large, multipurpose room. There are also district personnel, principals, and teachers from other schools, as well as the 16's parents. In all, there are nearly 60 people present.

One by one, the 16 introduce a specific movement that he or she has found helpful to stay focused while learning. But the 16 do not just model their chosen movement. They tell everyone in the room to get up from their seat to follow along. There are lots of smiles and laughter among the crowd.

It's now nearing the end of the training. Each of the 16 takes a turn coming to the microphone. Once there, they share a short reflection of their experience while learning in this new and different way.

None of the 16 have planned or rehearsed what they are going to say. They speak from their heart, explaining, for example, how before, they had truly thought they were stupid but how they now know they *are* smart. There is not a dry eye in the audience.

A large group of educators were now motivated to give many more students a chance to learn this way.

THE NEXT PHASE

The original plan had changed. At the start of the next school year, we opened the first official Brain Lab. The teachers from all grade levels at Paul Ecke Central were going to select various students from their classrooms to come to this Brain Lab for an hour each day. I would also provide trainings for the teachers so they could learn how to incorporate what I had done with my 16 in their own classrooms.

During this time, I kept learning more. For example, a whole new world opened when I started to learn about visual and auditory processing skills. It was no surprise that the Brain Lab kids also seemed to struggle in these areas. So I created fun visual and auditory processing activities that then became part of what we did in the Brain Lab.

Everyone was enthusiastic since the kids were most definitely showing improvement. And yet I couldn't help but notice that some of the kids weren't moving forward in certain areas. My original nagging question returned: Are we still missing something?

THE SEARCH CONTINUES

Esperanza, who was eight years old, was chosen to come to the Brain Lab—and she was probably one of the main reasons that I kept searching to learn more.

It is because of Esperanza that I only half-jokingly say that we should maybe buy insurance for the Brain Lab. That's because I've never met anyone who seems to be missing what would be considered automatic balance.

For example, in the Brain Lab, Esperanza jumps maybe twice

on the mini-trampoline before she literally falls off—and this happens nearly every time. She tries to walk across the low, rocking balance beam—but again, she falls almost immediately. Falling off chairs is also a routine event for Esperanza.

But this is also odd: Esperanza never seems to feel any pain when she falls. In fact, she's always laughing after a crash. (By now, I also notice how many other Brain Lab kids seem to have an exceptionally high tolerance for pain. I note that as one more mystifying common behavior among them.)

However, this is what Esperanza is most legendary for: She is in the third grade, but she still cannot count past nine. It does not matter how many people try to teach her or whether we integrate lots of movement and creative approaches when presenting lessons to her in the Brain Lab.

Whenever Esperanza counts, it's always the same. She gets to the number nine and then just continues with a string of random numbers (15, 19, 38)—with no awareness that she is no longer counting in order. In addition to that, Esperanza doesn't seem to grasp even the simplest math concepts, such as identifying coins or adding numbers. Again, it does not matter how much movement or creativity we integrate into such lessons.

After trying so many approaches, I finally tell the Brain Lab volunteers to quit asking Esperanza to count to 10 or to do any math activities with her. Yet I remain mystified as I keep searching for an explanation. There are clearly more missing pieces to this puzzle.

THE FIRST-YEAR-OF-LIFE CONNECTION

I honestly cannot recall how I came across the book *What to Do about Your Brain-Injured Child* or why I even decided to read it. After all, the Brain Lab kids were not "brain-injured." But for whatever reason, I read it.

While almost none of that book applied to the Brain Lab kids (and never ended up becoming part of the Brain Highways program), one part caught my attention. The book claimed that babies from all over the world did the exact same movements during the first year of life—but only if they were given an opportunity to move freely on the floor.

That book also made one important point quite clear: Movement during the first year of life was not only to ensure that babies eventually got up and walked. Specific movements also made it possible to integrate primitive reflexes and to develop the lower centers of the brain. Together, those movements created a strong foundation for the higher centers of the brain to build on while also wiring the brain to automate certain basic brain skills that are needed for nearly everything we do throughout our life.

My head was spinning. Had the Brain Lab kids missed out on these movements during their first year of life? Could *this* be the big missing piece to the puzzle?

DEVELOPING THE LOWER BRAIN

I still had no idea which specific early brain movements I would even have the Brain Lab kids do. Frustrated, I kept searching for more information.

Finally, I found a book that again I cannot explain why I chose to read. This one was called *If Kids Just Came with Instruction Sheets! Creating a World without Child Abuse.* On the basis of the title, nothing initially about this book seemed like it would be helpful for the Brain Lab kids.

Yet it turned out that this book had some interesting information on retained primitive reflexes. And near the end, I discovered the gold! There were five pages of instructions on how to recreate some of those early brain movements. At least I now had a loose framework to guide me.

But just as I was learning all this, a new word was getting buzz among the mainstream population. People were now talking about *neuroplasticity*, a rather formidable-sounding six-syllable word that simply meant the brain could change.

While neuroplasticity is today a well-known, documented fact, it was big news back then. With one swoop, neuroplasticity now erased the long-held view that the brain was hardwired and therefore could never change. To me, neuroplasticity meant that the Brain Lab kids could still integrate their retained primitive reflexes and complete their lower brain development.

To be clear, the general premise of recreating early brain movements to develop the lower brain was not something that I came up with on my own. With time, I did learn of a small number of people who were already helping others complete their lower brain development—and they had been doing so long before any of this ever came on my radar.

Yet the little that I was able to glean about these people's specific implementation and approach, the more I knew that just about everything they were doing would never fly *in public schools*. And so I boldly (or naively) began thinking about how I might change what was already being done so that the Brain Lab kids might benefit as well.

THANK YOU, IGNAZ

Figuring out how we might develop the lower brain in a school setting was just the first step. I also had to convince everyone that I hadn't lost my mind when I proposed that the Brain Lab kids would now do what looked like odd movements to integrate primitive reflexes, creep (the army commando crawl, with the chest and belly in contact with the floor), and then eventually crawl on all fours.

I first decided to share with everyone the true story of Ignaz Semmelweis, a doctor in the 1800s. That was before anyone knew germs existed and doctors routinely went from doing an autopsy to delivering a baby without ever washing their hands. When Semmelweis first introduced the idea of rigorous handwashing, he was ridiculed by all the other doctors. They didn't seem to care that the number of mothers dying after childbirth in Semmelweis's practice had plummeted since he started washing his own hands.

However, while what Semmelweis had advocated was novel back then (and turned out to be right), it was clearly not invasive or dangerous for doctors to wash their hands before anyone *proved* the existence of germs. And most importantly, the anecdotal evidence for handwashing appeared to be lifesaving to mothers.

In that same spirit I was now advocating for the Brain Lab students to naturally integrate primitive reflexes and finish their lower brain development. It would be our own neuroplasticity experiment. We would observe whether the Brain Lab kids could change their lower brain development, even though they were no longer babies. And I underscored that just as Semmelweis's new approach back then was harmless, what I was proposing was also not invasive or dangerous, and maybe—just maybe—it could bring about some remarkable changes.

I was given a green light.

ON THE FLOOR

Since we do not tell babies *how to creep*, we decided that the Brain Lab kids would also need to discover how to creep without any of us ever teaching them what to do. But right away, we were shocked at how the Brain Lab kids could barely move when they kept their chest and belly in contact with the floor. In fact, they looked much like very young babies when they first start to inch forward on their belly.

However, with time, we started noticing that the Brain Lab kids' creeping pattern was naturally evolving. For example, whereas it used to seem as though it took them forever to creep from one side of the room to the other, they were now gliding across the floor. It also did not go unnoticed that each of their creeping patterns had evolved *in the exact same way*—and that those changes happened without anyone ever telling or showing the Brain Lab kids how to move.

Once we observed that the kids' creeping pattern had significantly changed, we now added crawling (moving on all fours), since that's what babies do after they've been creeping. It was the same as when they started to creep. Over time, their crawling pattern changed—and again, in precisely the same way—even though we never told the Brain Lab kids how to crawl.

To us, the evidence was mounting: We are all innately wired to move this way.

ESPERANZA AGAIN

Not long after we observed those significant changes, something quite remarkable happened. That subgroup of Brain Lab kids—the ones who hadn't been progressing as much as the others—was now changing by leaps and bounds!

Yet it was Esperanza who became the most convincing reason for doing these early brain movements.

> Esperanza is gliding across the floor as she creeps from one end of the Brain Lab to the other. I honestly do not know why I'm thinking about doing what I am about to do. Maybe it's because we've seen how greatly Esperanza's balance has improved, and I am wondering if something else has changed. But I haven't thought about Esperanza's inability to count past nine for many months. Like I said, we had all quit asking her to do so.
>
> However, I now turn to Esperanza and say, "How about you count to 10 for us?"

Well, as always, Esperanza smiles as she starts counting aloud. As before, she has no problem getting to the number nine. But this time, after she says, "Nine," she says, "10, 11, 12" and then just keeps counting—*in order!*

The two Brain Lab volunteers and I drop our jaws. It is unbelievable!

Inspired by what we had just witnessed, the next day we decided to start teaching Esperanza the names of coins and their worth. No problem. Then we introduced simple addition facts. Again, no problem. What had changed? We couldn't come up with any credible answer other than Esperanza had begun to integrate primitive reflexes and develop the lower centers of her brain.

LOWER BRAIN SCREENINGS

Based on all I'd been observing, I came up with a simple lower brain development screening, and we began to screen all the kids at each grade level. The short version (I created several renditions) was fun and, best of all, took no more than five minutes to do. Yet it quickly and reliably told the teachers a lot about each child's lower brain development—specifically the way a lower brain connection might be affecting a student's ability to learn in the classroom.

But right from the start, these screenings made us pause and become even more curious. This was one of our first surprises.

Although it's the middle of the school year, six Indigenous kids from Guatemala have just enrolled at Paul Ecke Central. These kids are from three different families, and their ages range from five to seven.

Right away, we discover that none of these kids has ever gone to school in Guatemala. We also learn that they don't know how to read or write a single word—in any language. However, in terms of public-school classroom placement, none of that matters. Kids are generally assigned to a classroom based solely on their age, so these kids' classroom placements at Paul Ecke Central are no different.

Once each of them is placed in their respective classrooms, the kindergarten, first-grade, and second-grade teachers are understandably stressed. How are they supposed to teach these new, never-been-to-school students along with all the other kids in their classrooms?

Well, timing is often everything.

It turns out that we've already scheduled the primary-grade classrooms to participate in their first whole-class lower brain screenings. That date is in just a few days, so when the day arrives, the Guatemalan kids are screened along with everyone else. However, we're caught completely off guard (although the unexpected is becoming a regular theme of this journey) with their screening results. After watching so many of the American kids struggle with these simple challenges, the six Guatemalan kids sail through the entire screening, acing every one of the challenges!

This surprise immediately prompts us to look at the Guatemalan kids differently. No, they haven't had any formal education. But they're clearly neurologically wired to learn! The significance of their screening results is not lost on us.

In fact, one of the teachers says, "Now I think the Guatemalan kids will be easy to teach!" But then, recalling the number of students in her classroom who couldn't do many of the basic screening challenges, she says, "So the kids with no prior educational experiences are wired to learn, while the ones who have gone to preschool, along with experiencing so many other early childhood educational opportunities, are not." Although none of us deny the importance of those childhood experiences, we do appreciate the irony here.

So why did the Guatemalan kids sail through the screening challenges, whereas so many American kids struggled? Well, I had a theory, and it had nothing to do with being Guatemalan or American.

I speculated that it had more to do with how these different groups of kids had spent their early years of life. For starters, I learned that the Guatemalan kids had not lived in homes with baby apparatuses, wall-to-wall carpet, electronic toys, television, computers, and more—all which can collectively interfere with natural lower brain development. In contrast to those of the American kids, the Guatemalan kids' early years resembled more how babies and toddlers have always spent that time for most of history.

Okay, a sample size of six was clearly not enough to form any conclusions. Yet the stark contrast between the Guatemalan kids' early childhood experiences and the American kids' experiences during that same time was interesting.

As we screened more kids, we continued to be surprised. For example, there were kids, especially those in the younger grades, who the teachers had not considered to be among the students who struggled academically and who did not have behavior problems. Yet we were initially shocked as we watched how some of *those* kids also struggled during their screening. What could that mean?

We considered that perhaps those kids had inadvertently stumbled on ways to compensate for their incomplete lower brain development. That thought then prompted us to ponder the life span of compensations, noting that the academic expectations of each subsequent school year would increase. We started wondering, "Could this screening maybe even predict who might struggle down the line?"

We were also initially surprised at how quickly a five-minute screening could prompt a flood of compassion for kids who had previously been framed as not cooperative, not smart, not focused, not motivated, and more. But now the screenings were telling a different story. They revealed that many kids were trying to learn without one or more automatic, basic brain skills. And that's why after a screening, it was now common for teachers to say something such as, "Wow, I'm amazed that Zahara can even read and write at all!"

QUANTIFIABLE PRE- AND POST-SCREENING CHANGES

This is an important point about the screenings results: We never had the kids practice whatever screening challenges they could not do. That approach would have negated the whole premise of the lower brain connection—that we're supposed to *naturally* acquire basic brain skills as we develop our lower brain.

For example, when Jose first did the balance screening, he immediately wobbled and then dropped his foot to the floor just a few seconds after raising it. From a lower brain view, the answer was not to sign Jose up for gymnastics or have him spend each day practicing standing on one foot. Instead, finishing his *lower brain development* would give Jose a chance to naturally acquire automated balance (among other basic brain functions).

Once Jose finished most of his lower brain development, we had him repeat the balancing screening, along with other screening challenges he couldn't do automatically at the initial assessment. That is because time and time again, kids who couldn't do a screening challenge during their original assessment could do that same challenge effortlessly in their post-screening.

So we weren't surprised when we watched Jose easily balance on one foot—*while also engaging in a conversation*. Being able to do the latter is how we knew that Jose's balance had become automated.

Yet here was the best part of Jose's post-screening results: They also coincided with irrefutable changes in his daily life. Whereas Jose could not previously sit still or focus for more than a few minutes, his new *automated balance* now made it easy for him to remain still and stay engaged with tasks for notably long periods of time.

But how did *that* remarkable change correlate with Jose's new automated balance? Well, many people may not realize that sitting or standing still requires good automated balance. However, unless we are gymnasts, there's a limit to how much any of us can count on our balance. For example, suppose we are now challenged to *be still* as we stand on a high rope—while also reading a book. Suddenly, we become just like those who can't sit still on a chair and focus. On that high rope, we'll first start moving back and forth *because moving helps us balance*. There's also no way that we are going to focus on whatever we're trying to read. Our brain is much too preoccupied with *not falling*.

Of course, automated balance is just one of a myriad of lower brain functions that we need in order to focus, learn, show coordination, and so much more. But these pre– and post–lower brain screenings were now making it clear why so many kids had struggled.

While the initial screening gave us insights on how someone's lower brain was currently wired, the post-screenings and coinciding daily life changes convinced us of this reality. For many people, developing the lower brain is key for moving forward and experiencing lasting results.

WHAT CAME NEXT

Word about the lower brain connection started spreading quickly. Educators from other schools and districts were now eager to understand how a lower brain connection might explain their struggling students. These educators, along with the schools' parent volunteers, wanted to learn how to set up their own Brain Labs, as well as how to screen for lower brain development.

The teachers were especially motivated to learn how to screen for a possible lower brain connection. While it is not difficult to facilitate a Brain Highways lower brain screening, it does take practice. It's not that the screening instructions and format ever change, but *how people respond to each screening assessment* will vary greatly. That means screeners need to understand what those different responses mean in terms of a person's lower brain development.

That's why I began providing specific screening trainings at various schools. At these trainings, the teachers first practiced assessing one another. Then they each chose several students from their classrooms to be screened at one of our group training sessions. That gave the teachers a chance to practice facilitating a lower brain screening with me right alongside them.

Since the rest of the teachers would also watch those screenings, they were now able to see how often kids responded differently to the very same screening. Some of those responses were initially shocking to the teachers.

For example, a child's eyes might dart forward *and then backward* during a simple screening simulating a type of automatic eye movement needed to read, or both of the child's eyes would start to converge toward the center *and then one would turn and go off to the side*, or a child—who knew her body parts with her eyes opened— would put her hands *on her knees* when the screening instructions said to touch her ankles when her eyes were closed. The teachers were even more shocked by how these kids seemed completely unaware that they had done something bizarre. And since screeners always respond as though the child has aced the challenge, the teachers were further floored by how the kids beamed (as in "I sure rocked that!") when everyone applauded after whatever they did.

Of course, these blatant screening responses made it abundantly clear that such kids had not acquired whatever innate brain skill was targeted in that screening. But there were also many nuances and subtle clues to observe when facilitating a lower brain screening.

With practice, those kinds of responses also became as obvious to the teachers as the overt ones.

Altogether, there was a recurring theme: The teachers now realized that many kids in their classrooms had not acquired basic brain skills directly related to learning and paying attention. And yet these kids were still expected to learn and behave a certain way.

FROM THERE ON

I stayed in the public schools for five years. I continued to oversee Paul Ecke Central's Brain Lab, while I also acted as a consultant and teacher trainer for the staff and parents at other schools in the county.

And that is pretty much where the *lower brain connection* story ends, even though the *Brain Highways* story kept evolving until it became the program it is today. Some of those big changes included my decision to leave the public schools in 2004 to open a community Brain Highways Center in Encinitas, California. There, we offered fun, informative on-site family and adult classes, with people coming from all over San Diego County—and often from even farther away.

But since parents and professionals were still interested in learning how to facilitate a lower brain screening, I ended up recreating what we did in those earlier teacher-training sessions in what became our online screening course. Thanks to cyberspace, which makes it possible for online programs to reach people almost anywhere, as well as technology that makes it easy to watch videos and download written support information right in our homes, people worldwide are now able to learn how to screen for a possible lower brain connection. Best of all, this online course presents rich video footage featuring people of all ages doing live screenings. That way, course participants can watch much of what we've already observed in thousands of screenings. Such footage also includes many of the shocking ways people often respond to those simple screening challenges. It's one thing to read about such responses and quite another to *see* people doing them.

However, those who came to the Brain Highways Center also kept asking how a friend or family member who lived elsewhere might ever benefit from what they were learning in their family and adult courses. That's why we kept pondering how to make it possible for more people to access those programs. And that is how we ended up becoming Brain Highways Global, the online international program we are today.

WHAT HAS *NOT* CHANGED

While much about Brain Highways has evolved since we began over two decades ago, the lower brain component is no different. Current Brain Highways participants still finish their lower brain development in the same way that our earliest groups did (though we continue to come up with novel ways to keep this fun), and they experience the same amazing changes once they acquire those automatic brain functions. We still also use those same screenings (though usually the shortest version), but now we assess the adults' lower brain development as well.

However, here is what we had hoped would change in people's thinking about the lower brain but unfortunately remains the same: Many people still view creeping and crawling as (at best) optional movements that babies might do during their first year of life. For those who may like some ready-to-go answers to counter the position that creeping and crawling are insignificant movements, I present the following.

You will first likely hear this argument: Creeping and crawling cannot be essential because not all babies do these movements. Of course, part of that statement is true; not all babies creep and crawl.

However, leaping to the conclusion that "therefore, creeping and crawling must not be essential" is the kind of example instructors of a logic course might use to explain faulty deductive reasoning.

A more accurate statement would be that babies do not need to creep and crawl *to get up and walk.* From a survival view, it follows that the brain would find ways for babies to be upright—even if they glossed over important neurological development—because it will always be a more challenging world if we cannot walk. But I also wonder why such people do not ask the more interesting question: Since so many babies worldwide *do* creep and crawl, what might be a common theme among those who do not?

Those who minimize the importance of creeping and crawling will also often point to all the happy babies and toddlers who have skipped over these stages. ("See? No fallout.") However, I've never seen any evidence-based research—say, spanning 20 years—that followed babies who crept and crawled during their first year of life and compared them with those who did not. Yet comparative statistical studies are common in the world of research; for example, we now know that smokers have a 15 to 30 times greater probability of getting lung cancer compared to nonsmokers. So then, would there be statistical differences in learning and behavior between those who initially crept and crawled and those who did not? We don't know that answer because no one is doing those kinds of studies.

However, I do concur that there is also no evidence-based research that proves anything that I present in this chapter. In the scientific world, the term *evidence-based* refers to specific criteria of proof that aren't included in the general meaning of the word *evidence.* For example, the *Oxford English Dictionary* defines *evidence* (in a general sense) as "the facts, signs, or objects that make you believe that something is true."

We respectfully acknowledge that evidence-based data differs from the facts-and-signs kind of evidence. But that doesn't mean that no other kind of evidence has merit. After observing 20,000 participants, here's why we believe that creeping and crawling are essential early brain movements:

1. Thousands of our lower brain screenings have shown that many adults and kids cannot do simple brain challenges, while others can easily sail through them.

2. Our participants have shown remarkable differences in their pre– and post–lower brain screenings after they have integrated retained primitive reflexes, crept, and crawled. Such results have also coincided with notable positive changes in their daily life.

3. Our participants' creeping and crawling movements evolved naturally and in the exact progression as when babies are given a chance to move this way.

In addition to our experiences, many occupational and physical therapists often note a correlation between poor muscle tone and core strength among those who never crawled as babies, as well as how crawling provides early opportunities to practice cross-lateral movements needed for reading, writing, drawing, playing sports, putting on clothing, and doing other daily actions.

But perhaps this simple analogy explains why those who believe that creeping and crawling *are* essential movements will not be persuaded by those who claim otherwise: Suppose I have lived my entire life in Tahiti, which means that I've never seen snow. However, it would be faulty deductive reasoning if I now conclude, "Since I have never seen snow, snow does not exist." It will not matter how many times I insist that statement is true, or how loudly I say it, or how many times I write it. There are too many people in the world *who have already experienced snow* to be convinced otherwise—just as there are far too many people who have experienced remarkable results after returning to the floor to creep and crawl.

WHAT *IS* DIFFERENT

We like to think of learning as linear, but it's often messy (in a good way). In my case, I ended up learning a key important variable *for repairing the nervous system*—the lower brain connection—before I really knew anything about the nervous system. Go figure. No question that in those early days, I was clearly winging it as I tried to make sense of what kept incredibly changing right before our eyes.

You, on the other hand, do not have to clear lots of brambles to start a new trail. Since 20,000 people of all ages have already participated in the Brain Highways program, this is now a well-traveled path. Likewise, you don't have to wait for all the pieces of a mystery to fall in place. Unlike those who were game to change their brain in those early days—and had no clue how everything might play out— you already know the ending: Life is easier! (Since that is a hopeful ending, I don't consider it a problematic spoiler alert.)

However, there's still more important information about a possible lower brain connection. That's why the next chapter continues by focusing on all the ways this underdevelopment often shows up in our life.

7

∼∼∼∼∼∼

WHEN THE LOWER BRAIN
IS NOT ON PEOPLE'S RADAR

I t is mind-boggling how often a lower brain connection shows up in our lives. Yet most people are still unaware of this possibility. That means we could be the one who hasn't finished this development. But it could also be a family member, a neighbor, a work colleague— or all of us! That's because these days, it is rarer to find people who have finished this development during their first year of life than not.

When we haven't finished our lower brain development, we increase our probability of being stuck in protection mode. Since we need to do everything in life without certain automatic, basic brain functions in place, we are continuously stressed. Yes, sometimes our compensations work, but often they do not.

It gets worse. Recall that our cortex has no qualms about concocting not-so-nice stories to explain someone's actions. But without considering a possible lower brain connection, we will likely peg people in question as underachievers, or space invaders, or klutzes, or many other unattractive framings. We will also likely view ourselves negatively, perhaps thinking that we are dumb or lazy when we don't meet others' expectations.

So, what might an ordinary day look like when people are unaware of a possible lower brain connection? To give you an idea, I have created Kate and Shane, two fictional people who demonstrate many common behaviors among real people who haven't finished their lower brain development.

However, when reading about Kate's and Shane's day, it's helpful to remember that a wide range of behaviors may indicate a possible lower brain connection. While some people will share all of Kate's and Shane's behaviors (and others have even more challenges), it is also true that people who haven't finished their lower brain development may demonstrate a behavior that neither Kate nor Shane do, or they may only demonstrate one or two of their behaviors.

I first introduce you to Kate and what has happened in her life over a 30-hour time frame.

KATE: BEFORE, DURING, AND AFTER WORK

This morning, Kate is feeling tired. Thank goodness for caffeine! Last night was yet another one of those nights where she could not fall asleep until two in the morning.

Kate is still dragging by the time she arrives at work. She heads straight to the break room for some more coffee. Once there, she sees that several of her coworkers are sitting at a table.

As Kate reaches for a coffee cup, Jane casually mentions, "Kate, you're on break room cleanup duty this week." But Kate immediately snaps back, "When have I ever *not* cleaned up?" Kate is completely unaware that the others are taken aback by her disproportional response to what seemed to them merely a friendly reminder.

Once back in her cubicle, Kate is still ruminating over what Jane said to her. But Kate knows that she'd better get some work done. A big project sitting on her desk is due tomorrow morning. The truth is that Kate has been putting off this project for days now, partly because it requires a lot of reading.

Since childhood, Kate hasn't liked to read, mostly because it takes her a long time to comprehend whatever is on a page. Kate knows that she'll need to read and reread and reread the text related to the project before she's ever going to understand it. She also knows that after she has read the text for a while, the words on the page will start to move or shift together, which then makes everything even more challenging.

Plus, Kate keeps getting distracted—and it's more than just thinking about what Jane has said. There is that guy outside her window with a really *loud* leaf blower. There's Ken in the cubicle to her left, who keeps making one phone call after another, and there's Suzy in the cubicle to her right, who will not stop talking to Emiko about her daughter's upcoming wedding.

All these people are making it extremely difficult for Kate to concentrate. She is getting more and more irritated.

Finally, it's nearing the end of the workday, and most people are packing up to go home. But this is when Kate goes into high gear, when her adrenaline is really cranked up. She will stay late. She will pull an all-nighter, if necessary, to finish her project. Kate is used to working under pressure. In fact, she thrives when she's surging. After all, surging through all-nighters and caffeine are what got her through college.

Now, at one in the morning, Kate is finally home. But she is still wired and cannot fall asleep for a few more hours.

Once again, when her alarm rings at seven, Kate finds it challenging to wake up. But luckily coffee is always her friend. However, since Kate is dragging even more than usual this morning, she also eats two cinnamon rolls, which give her an extra sugar high. Kate, though, is in a good mood. She finished her project last night!

When Kate arrives at work, her boss is waiting for her. He has her project—the one she worked on until one in the morning—in his hand. But he doesn't look happy. "What is this?" he asks. Before Kate can answer, he says, "This is *not* the part of the project we needed done for today."

Kate starts to get defensive, but her boss immediately cuts her off. At this point, Kate is no longer listening to what he is saying. All she is thinking is, "I hate my boss. I hate my job. I hate my life."

WHAT REALLY HAPPENED (FROM A LOWER BRAIN AND NERVOUS SYSTEM VIEW)

Spending a lot of time in protection mode has affected Kate's cortisol levels and natural circadian rhythms. That's why her cortisol levels now rise at night (when they are supposed to drop), making it hard for Kate to fall asleep. But then those levels drop in the morning (when they are supposed to rise), making it hard for Kate to wake up.

Kate's poor vestibular processing (a common problem with incomplete lower brain development) makes it additionally challenging for her to awaken in the morning. That same lower brain connection is what prevented Kate from seeing the bigger picture, which is why she didn't understand which part of her project needed to be prioritized and what to work on first. It also prevented her from "letting go" of what she thought Jane said, from effectively filtering the background noises surrounding her cubicle, and from reading the project text with ease and speed.

A combination of Kate's incomplete lower brain development and inflexible nervous system also skews her neuroception. So Kate does not always read safety and danger cues accurately. That's why Kate "knew" that Jane's comment *was* mean-spirited and why Kate was also not able to read the rest of the room. If she had, she would have seen that everyone was surprised at *her* reactive response to Jane.

But Kate isn't aware of a lower brain connection or the possibility of being stuck in protection mode much of the time. So how does Kate explain what happened?

Well, she might blame her boss for not having the right report ready. After all, he did not tell her which part of the project was important. She may decide this last interaction with him proves that he is an all-time jerk. As for Jane, Kate may frame her as a snarky, bossy woman who thinks she knows everything.

However, Kate might also be incredibly harsh on herself, engaging in a litany of negative self-talk about what she "should have" done. Kate might even go down the victim path, where she views what has happened as just more proof that people (and life) are always out to get her. Of course, Kate could respond with all those reactions while noting that even one of those thoughts will keep her in protection mode.

SHANE: AT SCHOOL

It is Monday morning, and Ms. Miller calls Shane and a few other second graders to the small kidney-shaped table for some small group instruction. Shane chooses a seat to the far left of her. Almost immediately, Ms. Miller tells Shane, "Pay attention!" That's because he keeps looking everywhere—except at her.

Ms. Miller continues with the phonics lesson. But whenever she calls on Shane, he seems to have no understanding of short vowel sounds. When the lesson is over, Ms. Miller sends this group back to their seats as she calls another group to come forward.

That means it's now time for Shane to do independent work at his desk, which today is a writing assignment. But as soon as Shane sees the blank paper on his desk, he feels angst. Countless times before, he has experienced that writing is hard for him.

So instead of getting started, Shane now meanders across the room to sharpen his pencil. He's also in no hurry to return to his seat. But when he finally returns, Shane does start to write. However, after writing just two words, he thinks he made a mistake. Shane quickly erases what he wrote, but he uses so much force that the paper rips.

It's finally time for recess. Since Shane hasn't finished his writing assignment, he is worried that Ms. Miller is going to make him skip recess to complete it. But today she does not say anything. Happily, Shane runs out the door. Finally, he gets to move!

But recess is not all that great for Shane. He is never asked to play with the kids who are engaged in a soccer game, and he is not invited to join anyone else in whatever they are doing. Shane spends recess just walking around by himself.

When everyone is back in the classroom, Ms. Miller announces that the students will be taking a timed number-fact test. As soon as Ms. Miller says, "Go!" Shane looks at the paper with all the math problems—but his mind goes blank.

Shane starts to tilt his chair backward, since he has intuitively discovered that this position (along with rocking) helps him focus. But as he tilts the chair, he loses his balance and falls to the floor. Falling off a chair happens regularly to Shane—though he never knows why he cannot seem to stay seated.

However, Shane now reacts as he always does whenever this happens. He starts clowning around, giving the impression that he always intended to fall. Some kids in the class laugh, but Ms. Miller is not amused.

At the end of the day, Ms. Miller pulls Shane aside to talk to about his uncooperative, disruptive behavior during the day.

WHAT REALLY HAPPENED (FROM THE LOWER BRAIN AND NERVOUS SYSTEM VIEW)

It is important to note that Ms. Miller is neither a mean nor a bad teacher. Ms. Miller is just not aware of how a lower brain connection and being in protection mode can show up in a classroom.

For example, if Ms. Miller had such knowledge, she would have guided Shane to sit directly in front of her—rather than to her far left. She would have known that many kids with incomplete lower brain development see only the world that's right in front of them. Assigning Shane to the seat at the center of the table, directly across from her, would have made it easier for Shane to stay focused on her.

Ms. Miller would have also known that phonics lessons can be an unproductive, frustrating experience for kids with incomplete lower brain development. That's because such kids do not often have good auditory discrimination skills, one of many auditory processing skills that we're intended to acquire naturally with our lower brain development.

So when Ms. Miller asked Shane questions about various short vowel sounds, he had no clue what she was talking about. To Shane, all vowels sound the same. That's also why Shane cannot rely on phonics to spell or sound out words.

If Ms. Miller was aware of a lower brain connection, she would have modified the independent writing assignment for Shane. That's because when we're missing many automatic, basic brain skills (again, that we acquire naturally through lower brain development), writing is going to be far more challenging than it's ever supposed to be.

But without those modifications, it was no surprise that Shane shifted into protection mode at the mere thought of writing. While on some days his protective reaction reflects more of fight behavior, today Shane did flight behavior by taking his time to sharpen his pencil, thereby delaying having to write.

Shane also has poor proprioception, which is another common

problem when we do not finish our lower brain development. Among other ways that poor proprioception can show up in our life, it can interfere with our innate ability to reliably sense how much pressure we need to exert whenever doing various tasks. In contrast, if we have good proprioception, we've probably never thought about automatically knowing how much pressure we use throughout the day. We just naturally hold a glass, pick up a package by the front door, write and erase words on a piece of paper, and do everything else without a problem.

But that's not Shane. His poor proprioceptive processing is why he ripped his paper when erasing and why he pressed too hard when writing (which then made the words even harder to erase). Pressing so hard on his pencil is also why Shane often breaks its lead (though the upside here is that Shane now has another reason to delay writing by, once again, getting up to sharpen his pencil). Shane's poor proprioception is even why his classmates excluded him when they were out on the playground. They have experienced that Shane plays too roughly.

Shane's vestibular processing is also skewed, a common occurrence when the lower brain development is not completed. Shane's poor vestibular and proprioceptive processing explain why he keeps falling off his chair. His poor vestibular system first caused him to lose balance after he tilted his chair backward (which, recall, he does to pay better attention). But his poor proprioceptive processing caused his internal ground control to communicate too s-l-o-w-l-y. By the time Shane got the message "Falling! Make a quick adjustment!" he was already on the floor.

Of course, Shane doesn't understand why he keeps ending up on the floor. However, he has discovered that if he pretends that he planned to fall by clowning around, his classmates will laugh. Acting silly (even if it gets him in trouble) seems better than feeling embarrassed that he cannot even sit on a chair.

Now, if Ms. Miller understood all this, she would not think that Shane was playing around when he fell off his chair. Additionally, she would know that Shane is even more likely to fall off his chair whenever he *is* paying attention. That's because Shane's higher centers of the brain are not always able to focus and compensate for his poor vestibular and proprioceptive processing at the same time he is trying to learn. So, for Shane (as well as for many other kids), the directive "Sit still and pay attention" is not a biological option. For such kids, it's more accurate to say, "Sit still *or* pay attention."

But like Kate, Shane has no awareness of a lower brain connection or being stuck in protection mode. Shane's brain is left to concoct its own stories to explain what regularly happens to him. How then does a seven-year-old frame his behavior?

Well, unfortunately, I have heard that answer many times from kids who first start Brain Highways. These kids, some of whom are younger than seven, will tell me that they already know they are stupid, or lazy, or mean—and they make such statements as though these are facts set in concrete.

These kids (and others) also have no understanding that being in protection mode explains why they shut down at times, and why at other times they are combative and aggressive. But such behavior is what we would expect from a nervous system that is continually asked to do tasks that aren't within reach, especially knowing that a reprimand for not meeting expectations may follow.

Since these kids often feel as though their life is out of control, they may also compensate by being the ones who try to control everyone and everything. (If they control the narrative, they cannot fail.) Of course, that compensation only creates more problems. Since dominating, dictating kids are generally viewed in a negative way, they're now excluded from birthday parties, kicked off sports teams, and more as others frame them as rude and defiant.

Even at seven, Shane may have experienced some or all of that, which is why he has already mastered negative self-talk and says that he hates school. But not understanding the lower brain connection and being stuck in protection mode doesn't only affect Shane. If Ms. Miller understood all this as well, her day as a teacher would have also been much more enjoyable.

WHICH STORY?

Perhaps some people aren't ready to accept that a lower brain connection explains much of how Kate and Shane and others act. But knowing that the brain always likes to create a story for whatever happens, what are the alternative stories if a lower brain connection does not exist? Kate is a disorganized, high-maintenance, overly sensitive young woman? Shane is an unfocused, careless, disruptive seven-year-old? And if *those* stories are true, then why would Kate or Shane want to act that way? After all, their actions don't prompt others to respond to them in a positive way.

We also cannot forget that what we think is directly linked to how we feel and act. So if people adopt those possible stories as the truth, then what are the chances that they will ever view Kate and Shane and others like them with compassion? Will they instead demand that such people act as they have deemed to be appropriate? Will they then judge and criticize such people if they don't perform as expected? And if people adopt (and act) on *those* stories, what are the chances that everyone will not end up in protection mode?

On the other hand, when we consider a possible lower brain connection, we remain curious and compassionate. Most importantly, we now partner with such people as we help them compensate in supportive ways that address their current lower brain development. (Learning how to do this is the focus of Chapter 8.)

We start becoming convinced of a lower brain connection when we experience firsthand how making such modifications creates immediate positive changes. We become believers of a lower brain connection when we observe how those very same people no longer need that kind of assistance after they've completed that development. Of course, if we also learn how to do a lower brain assessment, we can additionally rely on those results to help us know whether we're observing a lower brain connection in daily interactions—or whether the behavior is caused by something else.

Note that we always say that we're looking for a *possible* lower brain connection. Clearly not every behavior is reflective of a lower brain connection. That's why, for example, Brain Highways participants learn how to differentiate between lower brain behaviors and learned automated stress reactions. Such distinctions are important because they each warrant a different kind of response to move forward. But other reasons can also explain a person's behavior. For example, hormonal imbalances and reactions to certain medications may cause a person to act in a certain way.

WHAT ABOUT A DIAGNOSIS?

What if you're thinking that Kate's and Shane's behaviors can be explained by a *diagnosis*, such as they have ADHD, or autism, or oppositional defiant disorder, or sensory processing disorder? While not everyone who participates in Brain Highways has a diagnosis, many do—and the number and different kinds of diagnoses over the years have greatly increased.

First, we cannot ignore that mental health has become a serious, huge, worldwide problem affecting millions of people. The absolute upside of having a mental health diagnosis is that people can then be directed to the right services and learn different ways to cope and manage their life.

However, sometimes a diagnosis also comes with an unintended downside. That happens when people are told (or believe) that a diagnosis now somehow limits or defines them. Along with that kind of thinking, people often accept that some behaviors are never going to change. In such cases, they may even expect that some people will randomly explode and act in violent ways if such behavior is common among those with certain diagnoses. For example, at Brain Highways, many kids were regularly engaging in behaviors such as screaming, biting, choking and clawing others, throwing chairs, and having complete meltdowns—sometimes as often as 10 times a day before they started our program.

I realize that I may be walking on a land mine as I continue here, but it is something I hope people will consider. I know that it's a commonly held belief that such kids do not "know" what they are doing when they are so explosive—and for others to suggest otherwise shows an intolerance and an inability to accept these kids for who they are. But we can equally make the case that accepting those behaviors as part of a diagnosis is also not seeing these kids as their true selves. It implies that such kids have only the survival parts of their nervous system but somehow missed out on the connection part of the nervous system.

Or the inference is that while these kids may have the connection part of their nervous system, their diagnosis precludes them from restoring its flexibility. Instead, we are to accept that they're just permanently wired to go from 1 to 100 in seconds. (To note, we don't need a diagnosis for that to happen. Think road rage and many other ways that people's behavior radically changes within seconds.)

However, at Brain Highways, protection-mode behaviors are just that—regardless of who is doing them. That means the only "story" when observing such behaviors is still "Once upon a time, the nervous system perceived a threat and responded in a protective way." So, with a wider view, we can have both a diagnosis *and* an inflexible nervous system. Yet an inflexible nervous system can also change so that it works as intended, and that process is possible for everyone.

I am not just being hopeful with that thought. That is exactly what we have observed, again and again, with such kids, regardless of their diagnosis or history of behavior. Once these kids restored their nervous system's flexibility, it was easy for them to show *who they really were* as they spent more and more time in connection mode.

Think about it: None of us can show up as our true selves when we are in protection mode. (Would any of us want to be framed by whatever we said or did while in protection mode?) And yet our protection-mode actions are often the basis for why people are convinced that they really do know us. Of course, that conclusion does not happen just for those with a diagnosis.

When widening our view, here is something else worth noting: Many behaviors associated with various diagnoses are often the same behaviors we observe in those who haven't completed their lower brain development. For example, an inability to make and sustain eye contact is often noted as common behavior among those with autism.

But people with autism are not the only ones who avoid eye contact. Making and sustaining natural eye contact is one of those basic skills acquired by completing the lower brain development. That's why it's possible to have autism *and* incomplete lower brain development. However, recognizing that possibility means that many of those overlapping behaviors *may now improve* once that development is completed.

In the early days of Brain Highways, I was humbled after realizing that I, too, had a limited view. This came to light when a parent of a child with Down syndrome wanted to participate in Brain Highways. I recall initially thinking, "Down syndrome is clearly a genetic diagnosis. Our program will not apply to her child." Thankfully, I didn't express my thoughts out loud. Instead, I just shared that we hadn't previously worked with any participants with Down syndrome, but we could see what might happen if she wanted to participate.

Well, this 10-year-old girl blew us away with her changes. Her speech, balance, motor skills, and ability to learn all greatly improved. No, her participation in Brain Highways did not change her Down syndrome diagnosis (that goal was never on the table). But it did make her life much easier. It did make it possible for her to shine and interact with others in new, exciting ways.

Since then, we have worked with many people with Down syndrome and related diagnoses, as well as those with actual brain injuries. Our view is always the same. We never challenge a diagnosis. We always just ask: Could this person's life be easier?

Of course, such changes are only possible because of neuroplasticity. I personally love that neuroplasticity is so accommodating and compatible with whatever we may already be doing—for example, there's no problem being on medication at the same time we are developing our lower brain. People do not ever have to choose one over the other. For that, I am grateful, especially since many Brain Highways participants are often on some type of medication. These participants will share that while their medication helps them in some ways, they are still struggling, which is why they have enrolled. (To note, I also assume there are people on medication who are doing great. I just do not meet them at Brain Highways.)

However, Brain Highways participants who are currently on medication usually want to know the answer to this question: "Will I be able to go off my meds once I have changed my brain and nervous system?" My first response is "We're only an educational program, so any specific discussion about your medication is always going to be between you and your doctor." Only then am I comfortable conveying what other Brain Highways participants have experienced and shared.

Yes, participants do regularly say that their doctors have either reduced their dosage or (more often) have taken them off their medication altogether. Those scenarios seem to coincide with the point when people who struggled with anxiety, depression, sleep, and focus regain their nervous system's flexibility (which included addressing their lower brain development). After these participants started experiencing lasting positive changes, they approached their doctors and explained what they had been doing. Not only were their doctors on board to reevaluate their prescriptions, but they were also very interested in how such changes came about. For those doctors, that's how a lower brain connection initially came on *their* radar, and it is the only explanation I have for why so many doctors—who we have never met—continue to refer their patients to us.

But here is the main point: Once we decide to consider that incomplete lower brain development and being stuck in protection mode might be interfering with our life, we widen our possibilities for change. That's because something incomplete can be completed. Something stuck can become unstuck.

Of course, with a neuroplasticity approach, it also doesn't matter if we prefer *not* to take medication or if we want to forego a formal diagnosis. Neuroplasticity is such a big tent that it only requires that we have a curiosity about changing our brain and nervous system and the belief that we each have the power to do so.

HOW COMPENSATIONS CAN CLOUD EVERYTHING

If we do not finish our lower brain development, our cortex will have to work overtime. That's because our cortex now needs to figure out ways to compensate for those missing automatic brain functions. But rather quickly, that scenario becomes problematic. Here's an analogy that explains why.

Suppose I tell you that you now need to take over my job—even though you have no clue what I do while I'm at work. Oh, and by the way, you still need to do your own job as well. With this untenable setup, are you surprised that you're terrible at my job, or when your own prior outstanding work performance goes downhill? And how can you give your full attention to either job when you are tired—very tired—almost all the time? Well, that's pretty much how it goes for a cortex that is doing double duty.

When we rely on compensations, our work and behavior can also be inconsistent. That's because sometimes our compensations work, and at other times they do not. We may even start out doing a task just fine, only to have everything fall apart midway.

But without pondering a possible a lower brain connection, inconsistencies in our performance and behavior will only baffle people. We ourselves may also not understand how we can be "on" sometimes yet "off" at other times. Without such knowledge, we and others may conclude that we just need to try harder or pay more attention.

And yet other people's compensations may work consistently well, so there are no concerns. However, we can't always count on those compensations to cover for those missing automatic functions. For example, there are predictable times when a person (whose compensations have been working well) might suddenly seem to fall apart, either in terms of work performance, or behavior, or both. Such times may be around the fourth or fifth grade (when academic challenges become notably harder as compared to the primary grades), during puberty (a time when the teenage brain is already chaotic), going off to college, starting a stressful job, and giving birth to a child (or after the second or third child).

The surest way to know whether we've completed our lower brain development—or whether we're compensating—is to be screened. Even the most masterful lower-brain compensators cannot outsmart a Brain Highways screening. That's because each of our screening challenges is intentionally designed to strip away any possible compensation. That way, we can truly observe which basic brain functions are present and which are missing.

Of course, learning the status of our lower brain development does not mean that we need to do anything with that information, now or later. But remaining completely in the dark leaves us vulnerable to possibly being blindsided by unexpected changes somewhere down the road.

NOT ME

We may glide past those times when compensations predictably fall apart because we *have* already finished our lower brain development. But here's another possibility: We developed a significant part (though not all) of our lower brain during our first year of life, *and* we have discovered some good, effective compensations. That combination is what then often makes it easy to conclude, "A lower brain connection might apply to other people—but not to me."

For example, there are parents in our family program who I have come to think of as the 50 Percenters. Recall that many of these parents admit they enrolled for their child and were merely game to also change their own brain and nervous system. But they did not (initially) think they would experience any changes for themselves. After all, they were doing fine.

When we screened these parents at the start of the program, many of them already had about 50 percent of their lower brain developed. Between that degree of development and adopting effective compensations, 50 Percenters can truly pull off almost anything. That means their work is consistently excellent, and they are the people that others think of as being grounded—*except when they get hit with multiple stressors all at once.* Then the 50 Percenters fall apart much like those with a lesser developed lower brain. These 50 Percenters readily admit this is true.

But once the 50 Percenters develop more of their lower brain, they often share something like "Wow. Yesterday I had three major stressors happen, one right after another. And yet I handled each crisis without ever flipping out!"

In a similar way, the COVID-19 pandemic revealed many lower-brain compensators who otherwise may have continued to go about life without notable problems. However, COVID's never-ending uncertainties, whiplash of changing rules, divisive perceptions, monumental losses, long periods of isolation—the list goes on—were enough to challenge any brain and nervous system. Then add all those ongoing stressors to a brain that's also compensating for unfinished lower brain development. Not surprisingly, many people's prior effective compensations weren't able to withstand the constant challenges of COVID.

Avoidance is another subtle, brilliant way to compensate for unfinished lower brain development. For example, as we age, it becomes easier to avoid whatever we do not do well. Or maybe we chose a profession that allows us to work at home, or one with limited interactions with others, which unknowingly may continue to perpetuate the illusion that *our* lower brain development must be completed. When everything is going well, why would we ever think that our lower brain isn't fully developed?

Sometimes people will reluctantly agree that perhaps some of their lower brain is not fully developed. But then they often want to separate themselves from those who they believe *definitely* have an underdeveloped brain. In such cases, these people may now think there is a different way for *them* to finish their lower brain development. For example, they assume that they would do a lower brain "lite" version of the process, as compared to what those *other* people would need to do.

I understand that sentiment, but that's not how the brain works. Whether we start with 10 percent or 75 percent of our lower brain developed, we all finish that development in the same way.

To use a football field as an analogy, we are always headed toward the end zone. In this case, we all benefit by finishing our lower brain development once and for all. However, *where we start*—for example, the 5-yard line on a football field is closer to the end zone than the 50-yard line—will most certainly influence how long it takes each of us to get there.

WHO WOULD HAVE THOUGHT?

It turns out that yours truly was in that group of unsuspecting compensators. But if you had asked me if I was compensating when we first started the Brain Labs, I would have looked at you with surprise. After all, I had never struggled at school, or with work, or with coordination, or with relationships.

Of course, if you had pressed me to come up with something that I avoided, I would have said, "Okay, I guess I avoid driving at night." That had been going on since my college days. After realizing that I couldn't see all that clearly when driving in the dark, I intentionally avoided night classes. But I never viewed that as a problem. I just enrolled in day classes, which was no big deal, since there were plenty to choose from. After that, I married Jim, who automatically drove us whenever we were out at night. So even if you got me to concede that night driving avoidance was a compensation, I still would have shrugged, as in who cares?

However, I did want the Brain Lab kids to see that anyone could improve their brain by doing primitive reflex movements, creeping, and crawling. In other words, I wanted to establish that no one was "too cool" to be on the floor. So I often joined them. But again, I did so under the umbrella of being a good sport, of being a role model. It honestly never crossed my mind that these same innate movements might also be helping my own brain.

And then this happened one evening.

I pick up the phone, and it's my 14-year-old daughter. She tells me that something has come up, so her friend's mom can no longer pick them up. My daughter now needs me to come and get them.

I immediately start to feel some angst. After all, it is *nighttime*, and I do not drive at night. Jim is out of town, so it's not an option for him to go. My mind starts racing for a way to get out of this. But what am I supposed to say? I have NDDD (nighttime driving deficit disorder)? The truth is that I have no plausible reason to say no, and I'm clearly the only one who's available. So I hear myself saying, "Okay, I'll be there soon."

Well, there's no turning back now. I have to drive in the dark. As I'm pulling out of my driveway, I'm most certainly worried.

And then the most amazing thing happens. It takes me a few minutes to concede to what is obvious, but as I keep driving along the road, there's no denying it. I can see quite clearly—even though it is *dark*! I am giddy.

By the time my daughter and her friend climb into the car, I'm so excited that I can no longer contain myself. As I'm driving—did I mention it was *dark*?—I start saying aloud comments such as "Look at me! I'm driving at *night!*" If I were not so enamored with my new skill, I would have noticed that my teenage daughter was horrified as her exuberant mother kept going on and on about merely driving in the dark.

How did I explain this unexpected, surprising change? Well, I could only conclude that somehow getting on the floor with the Brain Lab kids had changed my brain in a way that now made it easy for me to see clearly when driving at night. After all, I wasn't doing anything different except for those early brain movements.

However, this story doesn't end with that evening. A year later, I decided to open the Brain Highways Center. And so, for the next 16 years, whenever the last class ended, it was almost always dark outside. For 16 years I drove home—in the dark—almost every night after leaving the center.

And that scenario is why I share this story. Opening the Brain Highway Center was an amazing, incredible experience—one of the best decisions I've ever made in my life. However, I would have never met any of those inspiring, unique, remarkable kids and adults who ended up coming to the center if I hadn't been able to drive in the dark.

Yes, my husband is a great guy. But it would have been completely unrealistic to expect Jim to pick me up every night whenever I wrapped up the last class. And so my "insignificant compensation" (avoiding nighttime driving) would have been an immediate deal breaker when I first thought about opening a center.

ALL OF US

In this book, I present many stories of people who hadn't completed their lower brain development, as well as those who were also stuck in protection mode. I share both subtle and overt examples so that you can glean how many ways our lives may be affected.

Yes, some of those examples reflect people who may appear to have more extreme challenges than what most people experience. But I intentionally included those examples for two reasons.

First, I want people who are having similar experiences to have hope that they, too, can have an easier life. But such examples are equally applicable to those who don't struggle in the same way. That's because if addressing our brain and nervous system yields remarkable changes for people with *extreme* challenges, then think how much easier such changes will come about for those who are struggling in more moderate ways.

For example, if a nonverbal 12-year-old can start talking, then a 12-year-old who is just not very expressive can certainly become more articulate. If people who were homebound because they experienced panic attacks in public can now venture out in the world, then people who sometimes feel a bit anxious can certainly feel calmer.

As I keep emphasizing in this book, we are much more alike in terms of how our brain and nervous system are supposed to work than we are different. But I sometimes ponder whether a hesitancy to openly look at our brain and nervous system with curiosity (and zero judgment) reflects the same kind of reluctance that is often experienced when talking about mental health. While some progress has been made, there is still a lingering message that tells people to keep quiet about any mental health concern.

Not only do I hope that changes, but I dream of the day when chitchatting about our lower brain and protection-mode status is as commonplace as conversations about the weather and sports. I also hope that we will not assume that only people with a certain "profile" might benefit from finishing their lower brain development. That is why I'm so grateful for the thousands of people—who others probably thought would have never been among those who would change their brain and nervous system—who have already participated wholeheartedly in our program.

One special evening with a group of 12 medical doctors ended up becoming the model for the kind of curiosity and openness that makes it so easy to explore a possible lower brain connection. Here is what happened.

At the doctors' request (after seeing so many of their patients change by participating in our program), I have agreed to meet them at the Brain Highways Center. I will give a short overview of our program and then answer their questions.

But as soon as the doctors enter, I get this idea—which I probably should have thought through. However, I find myself suggesting to the group, "Why don't we start by me assessing each of your lower brain's status?" They seem eager and curious to learn that information about themselves.

While the doctors' lower brain screening results vary, most are in that predictable 50 Percenter club. However, a few have developed much more than 50 percent of their lower brain, while one doctor's lower brain is only 20 percent developed.

Now, when I said I probably should have thought this idea through, here's why: I realize that I have to tell them their percentages, which also means that I'm telling these doctors that they have not finished all their lower brain development. I'm thinking, "Great. Not awkward at all, right?"

Yet learning that their lower brain isn't fully developed only seems to fascinate these doctors. Now they also want me to do some of the other screenings, such as checking their eye teaming. Then they keep vacillating between asking questions related to their patients and what they want to know about their own brain profiles.

Well, this session is supposed to be a short evening presentation lasting from seven to eight o'clock. That's why I finally (but nicely) kick them out at eleven o'clock! But it was a fun evening and a sheer delight to be with a group of confident professionals who didn't view their lower brain status as anything more than intriguing.

Over the next few days, 2 of the 12 doctors, who happened to be among the oldest of that group, even signed up for our adult course. When recalling that compensations are often less effective as we age, it wasn't surprising that the older doctors felt more of a need to address their lower brain development right then rather than later. From what these older doctors shared with me, they weren't experiencing any difference or challenges when at work and attending to their patients. But they had started to notice some changes in other parts of their life. After our evening session, they were now motivated to finish their lower brain development.

Again, I only share this story with the hope that it will help people remain open and curious about their own lower brain status. If we do discover that our lower brain isn't fully developed, there is, of course, nothing to hide, defend, or protect, and there is no story to tell—other than "I did not finish my lower brain development during my first year of life."

WHILE AWARENESS IS A GREAT START . . .

An awareness of a possible lower brain connection creates immediate positive changes because we are now curious rather than judgmental about what we're observing. But we can go beyond merely having this awareness.

The brass ring is always going to be to finish the lower brain development once and for all, which is not a quick process. But until such highways are in place, it's important that whatever we do *in the meantime* makes it easier to stay in connection mode. That's why the next chapter presents many specific ways to make life easier—right away—for those who have not finished their lower brain development. When our brain is not preoccupied with seeking compensations and our stress alarm is not going off every time we're asked to do something not within reach, we can show up as who we really are.

8

~~~~~~~

IN THE MEANTIME

My initial teacher trainings focused primarily on helping teachers view behaviors in their classroom from the lens of a possible lower brain connection. Such awareness then motivated these teachers to make specific changes for their students.

However, the teachers would also quickly shift from thinking about their students to how this information applied to them or others in their life. While differing in specifics, the following scenario was common at almost every training.

I've finished my presentation, and I am starting to gather my materials. I look up to see a young teacher standing in front of me. She looks like she has been crying as she starts to speak.

"I've been married for five years, and my husband has never wanted to snuggle with me or show any kind of affection. It has caused so much pain in our marriage. I've always thought that there must be something wrong with me.

"But as you were sharing a common profile of people who

haven't completed their lower brain development, I was checking off so many boxes in my head, thinking, 'That's my husband.'
And then you said that such people often register light touch as
unpleasant or even as repulsive. That's when I started to lose it."

She is crying now, and it takes her a moment before she continues. "You explained why my husband has never been able to
snuggle. It's not because of me. It's because he has never finished
his lower brain development."

As a side note, parents, too, are usually baffled and hurt when
their child won't snuggle or are embarrassed when their child quickly
pulls away after Aunt Tilly places a light kiss on their child's cheek.
Yet these distorted touch behaviors all make sense from the lens of
incomplete lower brain development.

Of course, distorted touch perceptions also change by completing the lower brain development. I remember a mom who was
crying (but this time happy tears) when she told me what had
recently happened with her eight-year-old son: "Best Christmas
present ever! My son—all on his own—climbed on the couch on
Christmas morning and started snuggling with me *for the first time
in his entire life!*"

WHEN AWARENESS ALONE IS EMPOWERING

Not only is awareness of a lower brain connection empowering, but
such understanding does not require anyone else to have the same
knowledge. That's what Marco, a fourth grader, discovered after
being in the Brain Highways program for just two weeks.

Marco wants to tell me what happened at school that day. "I was
tapping my foot on the floor while my teacher was teaching the
math lesson. And then she told me, 'Marco, stop tapping your foot!'

So I asked if there was another way that I could stimulate my pro-prioceptive system, you know, so I could stay focused on what she was saying."

Trying to hide my smile, I share with Marco that I'm glad he already understands what his brain is needing. Since I'm curious how his teacher responded, I ask, "What did your teacher say?"

Marco shrugs his shoulders. "Oh, she just shook her head and said, 'Whatever.'" (Translation: "I have no idea what a proprioceptive system is—but I am not going to admit that.")

This story is important for many reasons. First, it did not matter whether Marco's *teacher* understood why he was tapping his foot. Marco knew that he wasn't trying to be disruptive. Marco also knew that he was not a "bad" kid—and both thoughts are likely why Marco didn't shift into protection mode as soon as he was singled out.

But that same awareness also motivated Marco to learn simple ways to stimulate his proprioceptive system that did not draw attention to himself or require his teacher's help. And as Marco continued to develop his lower brain, he no longer needed such compensations. When the lower brain is developed, proprioceptive processing naturally improves.

WHAT WE CAN DO RIGHT NOW

If people haven't finished their lower brain development, we can do many specific actions to make it easier for them to learn, focus, complete tasks, and have positive interactions with others. Collectively, such actions also help keep everyone in connection mode. The rest of this chapter presents some of the many ways we can do this.

Ways to Move

Our vestibular and proprioceptive sensory systems are just as real as our visual, touch, taste, smell, and auditory senses. But if we haven't completed our lower brain development, these systems are not likely working as intended—and that's often problematic.

For starters, our vestibular system plays a big-time role in keeping us alert. To wake up a sluggish vestibular system, we can rock, spin, swing, jump, bounce, run, hang upside down, and even just move our head up and down, as well as from side to side. While notably not the norm, we might also spin or jump as we walk from one room to the next, rock as we're listening to directions, and do head movements while seated in front of the computer. Such actions will keep a sluggish vestibular system awake.

To note, some people have the opposite of a vestibular system that needs more stimuli. Instead, these people are bombarded with too much sensory information. So, unlike those who crave movement, they prefer to be stationary. While most of these same vestibular movements also benefit them, they're helpful only if such people do them very s-l-o-w-l-y and for only a brief time. Of course, completing the lower brain development is the most natural, efficient way to improve vestibular processing and experience lasting changes.

We also need good proprioceptive processing. This sensory system gives us an innate "knowing" of where our body parts are and what they're always doing. It also allows us to intuitively recognize spatial boundaries and how much pressure we need when handling objects or making physical contact with others. When our proprioceptive system is working as intended, specific receptors of the skin, joints, and muscles provide this information both accurately and efficiently.

However, if we don't receive good, accurate proprioceptive information, we may be known as a space invader, or a bull in a china shop, or a klutz, or a child who plays too roughly with other kids and pets, or a child who chews on hoodie strings and shirts, or someone who is often tapping his hand or foot (like Marco).

Completing the lower brain development also naturally improves our proprioceptive processing. In the meantime, pushing, squeezing, pulling, pressing, and carrying heavy loads can be helpful. Engaging in pillow fights, doing wheelbarrow walks, playing tug-of-war, squeezing putty, kneading pizza dough, vacuuming, mopping, and doing push-ups are more examples of ways to stimulate our proprioceptive system. Even something like chewing gum can be a great way to provide proprioceptive stimuli. However, don't be surprised if those with poor proprioceptive processing require a lot of gum (maybe even three pieces) before gum chewing has a notable effect.

Weighted Blankets

I first experienced that weighted blankets are a great source of proprioceptive stimuli when I was facilitating the Brain Lab. At the time, I had just read about them, but I had no clue if they were effective. I was curious, so I asked a friend to make six weighted blankets for the Brain Lab.

Since school has already started, everyone is inside their classroom. I'm walking toward the Brain Lab carrying the last of the new weighted blankets when I see a parent and her child in the near distance. They are outside the kindergarten classroom, and the child is screaming while clinging to his mom. I do not know either of them.

The mother sees me and calls out, "You're the Brain Lady, right?" I try not to smile at her reference to me (I am hardly the "brain lady") because I can see the desperation on her face. "Please help me!" she begs. "I can't get my son to go into his classroom."

Even though this child is not a Brain Lab participant, I do not see any reason not to help her. Besides, I still have about 15 minutes before I start working with my first group of kids. So I invite the mom and her son into the Brain Lab.

Her son is still screaming. It's then that I get this idea. Why not put one of the new weighted blankets on top of his back? While he hasn't stopped screaming, he does willingly lie on his stomach. I put the weighted blanket on top of him.

And it's like magic. Almost instantly, he stops crying. I leave the weighted blanket on him while his mother and I stay quiet. He does not move, but we rather quickly start to notice that the lower part of his back begins to slowly rise, up and down, as though he is doing rhythmic deep breathing. After about 10 minutes, I take the weighted blanket off him. He is actually smiling now and says that he's ready to go to his class.

At that moment, I wasn't sure what I had just observed. But I was positive that the weighted blankets were staying.

What to Leave Alone

Once we understand how a behavior is connected to incomplete lower brain development, we can opt to leave those behaviors alone, so long as they are harmless and not disruptive to others. That means we now no longer insist that such people act in ways that are truly not in sync with how their brain is presently wired. For example, we can choose to no longer require others to make eye contact with us as we are talking. Such people's preference to look away (instead of at us) is an example of a harmless lower brain compensation that we can now leave alone.

Of course, whenever we say to a child, "Look at me when I am talking to you," we're really saying, "I need you to pay attention."

Yet, ironically, forcing people with incomplete lower brain development to make eye contact greatly decreases their ability to focus. That's because their cortex cannot pay full attention to whatever we're saying while it also needs to figure out how to make and sustain the eye contact.

Another simple leave-it-alone behavior for those with incomplete lower brain development is to allow such people to rock (if they choose to do so) when seated or standing. That's because, as noted, rocking helps many people keep their sluggish vestibular system awake, which then makes it easier for them to focus and process other sensory information.

However, just as people are unaware of a lower brain connection when they say, "Look at me when I am talking," teachers, parents, and others will often say, "Stop rocking!" whenever someone is not still. Again, the underlying thought behind that directive assumes that it's easier to pay attention if we're still. For some people, that is true. Yet for others, telling them to be still is the same as saying, "Zone out."

That's why, during a three-part training for teachers, I included that information on their first day. Well, right before the start of the second training (a few days later), one of the teachers came up to me, excited to share what had happened since that first training.

"I have this student named Joey, and he has been driving me nuts all year. That's because Joey is always *moving*—he really cannot be still. So, yes, I've been on his case.

"But yesterday, he was trying to tell me something. As usual, he was rocking back and forth, side to side, just like he always does. Yet this time I saw what he was doing so differently! Instead of telling him, 'Stop rocking!'—like I've done a zillion times this year—I said nothing. Instead, I was just thinking, 'You, go, little Joey! Do whatever you need so you can focus on what you are saying!'"

This teacher is beaming, as though she's just crossed a Rubicon that's going to forever change how she teaches.

But here is the truth: That simple decision has also made Joey's life in this classroom irrefutably better. For starters, Joey can now freely express himself, since being still is no longer required of him. He is going to process more easily whatever information his teacher presents, since he won't be zoned out. He will not feel as though he irritates his teacher (like all the time) or be frustrated with himself every time he tries to be still but ends up moving.

Of course, there are many more harmless, not disruptive, leave-it-alone lower brain behaviors. But here is what each has in common: Every time we choose to leave alone one of those compensatory behaviors, we are acknowledging and honoring the reality that *we are not all wired in the same way.*

Too Challenging to Leave Alone

Okay, even with the best of intentions, there may be times when our own brain profile and nervous system are going to find someone's harmless compensatory lower brain behavior just too distracting to leave alone. That is when we do something that we refer to at Brain Highways as "building into the structure." This simply means that we come up with a solution to meet the needs of whomever is doing the behavior—but also keeps us in connection mode.

For example, suppose we're around someone who is constantly humming, making noises, or talking under their breath. Yes, now we understand that's what many people do to create white noise when they can't filter all the auditory sensory information bombarding their brain. But now (since we are thinking of ways to build into the structure), we may suggest that this person wear headphones while listening to music. That, too, creates white noise that will block out random auditory sensory information. But our nervous system also gets the quiet that it needs.

Or maybe we feel on edge whenever we see a child fidget or slouch or rock in a chair—even though we now know that this helps them stay focused. But if there's available space, why not allow such kids to do their schoolwork or homework while sprawled on the floor? Or maybe we feel irritated every time we see kids touching everything in sight—even though we know that's a common compensation among many kids with incomplete lower brain development. Well, now we clear those kids' workspaces so that nothing is within reach. We also wait to pass out whatever until *after* we've given directions. That way, there's nothing to be distracted by while we are talking.

Building into the structure can really be that simple—and there are endless ways we can do so.

Predict, Preempt, and Enjoy

Building into the structure can also be thought of as a mindset. We first predict what someone will likely do and then preempt that behavior by doing something different. That then makes it easy for everyone to stay in connection mode.

For example, we may have previously thought our child or someone else was dissing us when they did not answer our question. We didn't understand that those with incomplete lower brain development pretty much live in a world confined to what is directly in front of them. So now we preempt that predictable scenario by making sure *we are directly in front of that person* before we ever start talking.

Or we may have previously told our son, "Gabe, go upstairs, get your field trip paper out of your backpack, and then bring it back downstairs for me to sign." In the past, we did not understand that Gabe's brain was still processing that first direction while we were already rattling off the second and third. We were then predictably annoyed when Gabe never returned with his field trip paper, which only reinforced our prior belief that Gabe never listens. But again, we can preempt that inevitable scenario by giving Gabe just one short direction at a time.

Chucking Two Directions

If we toss out two common directions, we already make life easier for those with incomplete lower brain development. That's because these seemingly innocuous phrases almost inevitably trigger such people's stress alarm.

The first direction is when we tell them to "try harder." Even though we think we are being encouraging, those two words will trigger hundreds, maybe even thousands, of memories when trying harder in the past has made no difference whatsoever. Now, instead of viewing that person as not putting forth enough effort, we modify or peel back the task so that the person can move forward more easily.

The second direction is when we tell such people to "pay attention." Until the lower brain is developed, paying and sustaining attention are often out of reach. That's why we put the focus on ourselves rather than expect the person with incomplete lower brain development to miraculously change. We now think, "How might I catch this person's attention?" That answer is then guided by what we already know about incomplete lower brain development and how that person's brain is currently wired.

Not to Forget the Obvious

Of course, we can ask people what we might do to make life easier for them. When we do that, we may be surprised at their answers. For example, a child might ask her mom to limit the number of errands they go on. The child shares that the sensory stimuli in so many stores keep bombarding her brain until she just can't take it anymore. This action helps the mom as well. Limiting the number of errands increases the chances that they both will stay in connection mode while they are out and about.

Of course, building into the structure is not only for kids. Many adults are also trying to function without basic brain functions, whether they realize it or not. It will only increase productivity and a positive, supportive working environment when employers and coworkers also build into the structure. Similarly, we can build into the structure for our partners, family members, and friends to circumvent predictable scenarios that *we already know* will create a disconnection.

NO GETTING AROUND IT

You may be relieved to have learned that certain behaviors are based on biology rather than personal flaws or preferences. And yes, there are many ways to make life easier for those who haven't completed their lower brain connection. But doing so will never be better than finishing this development. That is what creates a strong foundation for the higher centers of the brain to build on. That is what makes it possible to acquire those automatic, basic brain skills.

The last chapter of this section focuses on how we go about finishing our lower brain development if that hasn't happened. Recall that this is a huge variable when it comes to restoring our nervous system's flexibility. Acquiring those automatic, basic brain functions plays an undeniable role in reducing our overall daily stress. Best of all, we will no longer need others to anticipate and preempt for us. Realistically, we cannot count on everyone to respond this way. So, without finishing our lower brain development, we're always at risk for being misunderstood much of the time.

But most importantly, our cortex will be like, "F-i-n-a-l-l-y. I'll get to do my own job without distractions!" And when that happens, who knows what we might now be able to learn, what creative ideas will flow from us, and how much of our overall life will change?

9

CHANGING THE LOWER BRAIN

In today's world of apps, Google, and YouTube videos, we expect to find whatever information we want shortly after we start to search for it. Yet when it comes to learning how to complete our lower brain development, it doesn't work that way.

Sure, I could share lots of photos of babies doing primitive reflex movements, such as how all babies (not coincidentally) are in the exact same position to integrate what is called the asymmetrical tonic neck reflex. I can tell you that creeping across the floor is how babies first move from one place to another. I can tell you that babies then crawl on all fours, which is the second primary movement that develops the lower brain.

I can also share that if babies spend lots of their awake time on their bellies, those movements will evolve naturally in a predictable, observable pattern. This is true for babies all over the world. But here's what's even more remarkable: When we go back and develop the lower centers of the brain later in life, those innate patterns evolve *in the exact same order* as babies progress.

Now, with such information, you might conclude, "Great! I'll just

Google primitive reflex movements and natural creeping and crawling stages, and I'll know how to develop my lower centers of the brain." But unfortunately, it's not that simple. So, for those who might be considering flying solo, I break down the possible problematic scenarios that can interfere with this process.

THE TIME TRAP

It is wildly inaccurate to ever say that we have been developing our lower brain for three months, or six months, or for however long it has been since we first began. Those references only reflect how much *chronological time* has passed. But that has nothing to do with how much time we have truly spent doing the early brain movements. After all, we were clearly not developing our lower brain while we were eating, showering, watching movies, and doing just about everything else we might do in any given day during the span of that chronological time. That is why it's only accurate to record and refer to the number of collective hours we've spent doing those specific early brain movements.

But even knowing that information, we might wake up one morning with temporary amnesia and suddenly think we should have experienced more changes by now—you know, since we've been developing our lower brain for *two months*. So, without someone guiding the process (and gently reminding us that chronological time does not count), such a thought could easily trigger someone to quit, without ever reaping all the benefits still on the horizon.

CORRELATING CHANGES
WITH DEVELOPMENT

It's important that the person guiding the lower brain development knows which specific changes typically correlate with each stage.

Such guidance is like the way new parents rely on their pediatrician to know when a baby would normally roll over, sit up, and more.

Here is an example of a predictable correlation that may apply when developing the lower brain. Some (but not all) people who have not completed their lower brain development can have an extraordinarily high tolerance to physical pain. For example, such people may have even broken an arm yet felt nothing more than a little discomfort.

While that may not initially seem problematic, it is. Pain is supposed to help us pay attention to our bodies so that we can then address whatever has been hurt. Pain also prevents us from inadvertently injuring that body part even more.

Yet most people have never considered a correlation between a high tolerance to physical pain and significant incomplete lower brain development. In fact, I remember a dad who rather liked that his seven-year-old was such a "tough guy" when his family started Brain Highways. This dad would proudly note how his son had broken body parts, fallen out of trees, and more—and never cried.

But after this boy had clocked about 50 hours of the lower brain work, his dad was shocked that his son was now crying over what (in comparison to his other incidents) seemed like minor occurrences. What had changed? Well, his son's creeping pattern had evolved to the last stages. His seven-year-old had finally acquired the basic neural circuitry that now enabled him to feel physical pain as most people do.

Carly also had an unusually high tolerance for pain when we first met her. She was a 15-year-old who had been self-mutilating for quite some time. Understandably, this behavior greatly concerned her parents. Of course, when we assessed Carly, none of the staff were surprised to discover that her lower brain was significantly underdeveloped. We had already worked with many other teens and young adults who engaged in similar behavior when we first met them. (To note, while not everyone with very little lower brain development engages in self-injurious behavior, we've never met anyone who does this *and* has already completed their lower brain development.)

Carly was open to developing her lower centers of the brain. Since she enjoyed talking to me whenever she was at the Brain Highways Center, we established a good relationship over time. It had been almost two months since Carly had engaged in any self-injurious behavior—and then this happened.

> I open an email from Carly's mom, and she is clearly panicking. She writes that Carly and she were in a fight, and not long after, Carly had once again made cuts in her arm. But I pause because I have recently assessed Carly's creeping pattern, and it's now at the advanced stages. That's why I am wondering how Carly could have returned to her prior behavior without feeling a lot of pain as she cut herself.
>
> The next day, Carly is at the Brain Highways Center. I pull her aside, and I'm honest with her. I say that I'm surprised that she is still able to cut herself without much pain since she now has so many of her lower brain highways in place.
>
> Carly gives me a conspiratorial smile as she says, "No, it *did* hurt! That's why I had to be clever on *how* I cut this time—and make my cuts more superficial than before."

I share this story for three reasons. First, I want to keep under-scoring how many basic brain functions we may take for granted—in this case, feeling physical pain—that are related to lower brain development. But I also want to equally emphasize that not every behavior is related to such underdevelopment.

Here, Carly already knew that her prior cutting had horrified her mom. Carly's choice to self-injure herself *at this point in her life* was now an intentional way to get back at her mom. It was not a reflection of incomplete lower brain development, in which the brain's desperate need to "feel" something may be the motivation for cutting the body. That's why understanding where Carly was in her lower brain development became key to knowing how to move this situation forward.

The third reason I share Carly's story is to reiterate what we often say to our participants. A lower brain connection is not *always* the motivation or explanation for every behavior. For example, there are other reasons why someone may engage in self-injurious behavior. With that in mind, participants should never rule out enlisting other services, such as professional counseling, as needed. At Brain Highways, we always stay in our lane, meaning that we are clear what is beyond the scope of what an educational program can offer.

CORTEX CHALLENGES

When we go back to develop our lower brain after we are infants, our need-to-know cortex often gets in the way. For example, since we are not babies, we naturally think, "Okay, so what do those final early brain movements look like?" Our participants initially ask that question all the time.

While that sounds like a reasonable question, we discovered that it was more than mere curiosity. Whether it was conscious or subconscious, it appeared that participants wanted to know that answer so they could then try to replicate the final creeping or crawling stages. I think they thought that by doing the ultimately evolved pattern right from the start—rather than allowing it to progress naturally, all on its own, as babies do—they could expedite their development.

However, first they didn't realize that those trained to observe each notable nuance of the natural brain movements immediately know when someone's "cortex" is initiating the movement. When the lower brain development progresses naturally, the early brain movements do not look the same as when the cortex gets involved.

But more importantly, we are doing these lower brain movements to acquire automatic brain functions (not to just "look good" when we're on the floor). So why would we want to mess with the natural process? In other words, if we want to experience changes, we need to start wherever we left off as a baby. We need to allow our lower brain to develop in the way that we are innately wired for this to happen.

Our cortex is also not thrilled with the slow, tedious movement that reflects the earliest stages of creeping. Since we're generally inclined to think that faster is better, participants will often actively seek (or accidentally discover) compensations that now help them move more quickly across the floor. They will even say, "Wow! Creeping is so much easier now!" And away they go! However, that's when we smile and politely say to those Brain Highways participants, "Yes, you *are* moving faster, but that's more like sweeping the floor than developing your lower brain."

This is when having someone initially guide the lower brain development is helpful. Even though creeping with compensations slows the lower brain development, it is still never helpful to tell someone *how* to creep. The brain always needs to figure that out all on its own. But someone with experience will know how to help people end their compensations—and do that without ever revealing any top secrets.

A SOMETIMES-ROCKY START

Some people, but certainly not all, will go through a temporary period when it seems as though their prior behaviors have intensified. For example, kids who may have previously rocked a bit when seated in a chair may now rock like they're on a boat on choppy water. For a short time, people may also engage in what seems like inexplicable behavior, such as becoming very emotional over something or suddenly experiencing some brain fog.

I liken this brief period to when we start to clean a messy closet, and we're at that stage when we've taken everything out of the closet and thrown it into the middle of the room. Now, if someone happens to enter the room right then—well, everything seems worse than before. Yet this is all just part of the reorganizing-the-closet process.

In the same way, the beginning stage of developing the lower brain can be a bit messy for some people (again, not everyone experiences this short, muddled period) because our lives are different when we go back to finish this development than when we were babies. After all, babies do not go to school, work, soccer practice, and more. Someone skilled in guiding the lower brain development will be able not only to reassure such people that this "messy period" is common and *temporary* but to show them ways to stay grounded during this time.

OVERCOMING RESISTANCE

Although the benefits of developing the lower brain are huge, for various reasons some people may initially resist doing these early brain movements. First, most people already have packed daily schedules. So right from the get-go, some people might become combative when simply discussing how they could ever find time to creep each day. (Creeping needs to be done daily until a significant part of the pattern has evolved, but there's more flexibility once we begin to crawl.)

Plus, many people feel overwhelmed before they even start our program, which is why we encourage our participants to make a trade by temporarily putting something else in their life on hold. That way, they ensure that they will have a block of time to do the early brain movements at home each day of the week—but without adding any additional stress.

Setting aside this time is key because it's not as though we are going to creep as we go out the door to our car, or up and down grocery aisles, or anywhere else during our day. Doing the lower brain movements is always going to be "extra" in our life. There is no getting around that we will need to find time to do this, since we do not do any of these movements during an ordinary day. We also need to acknowledge that getting back on the floor to creep and crawl is not most people's idea of rip-roaring fun. That's why we offer our Brain Highways participants lots of creative, entertaining ways to keep their cortex engaged while creeping and crawling, but without disrupting the natural brain development.

It's additionally our experience that simply assuming or expecting that kids and adults will comply merely because someone has said, "This will be good for you," does not work. Instead, we have found that people are less likely to resist if they also engage in fun ways to learn why they would want to finish this development. That's why our participants also watch humorous videos, listen to audios with lots of stories, and review fun infographics.

In other words, people are less likely to resist investing in the kind of time that it takes to complete their lower brain development if they know how *their own life* could specifically improve by doing so. Knowledge of the lower brain also helps people when others look at them like they have lost their mind ("You're doing *what?*") if they share that they are now creeping and crawling to change their brain.

And then, there is always this catch-22 when people go back to develop this survival part of the brain: As a result of trying to forge through life without many automatic, basic brain functions, there is a high probability that their brain is already currently wired to automatically resist *anything* that is new, different, or challenging. That's why it is equally important to initially include ways to help the nervous system feel that it's safe to complete the lower brain development.

CHOOSING A PROGRAM

Today there are many brain programs, and they differ in format, time commitment, cost, and support, as well as who participates (are parents active or passive participants?) and even which part of the brain is primarily addressed (lower or higher centers of the brain?). Such diversity offers people many options.

Choosing one is not about which program is "better" than another. It's about finding a program that's a good fit for you. However, in making that assessment, it can be helpful to ask questions so that you can then differentiate between the programs that you're considering.

If you decide that you want to complete your lower brain development, you now have enough information to discern whether developing the lower brain is a primary component of whatever program you're considering. I also encourage you to establish your own criteria and guidelines for how you will go about choosing a program.

For example, when creating the Brain Highways program, I decided to include only lower brain movements that babies do naturally. However, I'm aware that some brain programs present primitive reflex movements that do not resemble anything that babies have ever done or that their physiology would make it possible to do.

One particular movement comes to mind: Participants are instructed to *walk* as they move their arms and legs in a specific unnatural way (which also requires a lot of higher brain development to do). To date, I've never been able to glean how that movement integrates any retained primitive reflex, which is not the same as saying that it does not accomplish that. However, per my criteria of replicating only what babies naturally do, this movement (or any other movements that babies do not do) wouldn't be part of developing the lower brain in the Brain Highways program.

Finally, people might (unknowingly) falsely assume that one brain program must be like another program if at first glance they latch on to something they think is common to both programs. Of course, sometimes that conclusion is true—while at other times, the format, presentation, content, type of support, and more are so wildly different between the two programs that they, at best, share only a general premise (as in *the brain can change*).

For example, I do know of a few programs that also focus on developing the lower brain, though such programs usually refer to this process as neurological reorganization or neurodevelopmental movement. Brain Highways and these programs share the overall belief that we can change the brain by finishing the lower brain development. But that's it. That's all I've ever found us to have in common with these programs. We're uniquely different in countless ways from any program out there. That doesn't mean that other programs aren't effective. It just means that it's not accurate to apply whatever someone believes to be true about any of those other programs—positive or negative—to Brain Highways, or vice versa.

SIMPLE—AND NOT SO SIMPLE

On one hand, it's remarkable that the same innate movements that babies do can develop our lower brain *at any age*. Even more remarkable is that once we have those highways, we have them for life. (There is no maintenance plan here.) And yet, as I've described, there are also many ways we might unknowingly go rogue if we try to develop our lower centers of the brain without any guidance and individualized feedback.

My biggest concern about flying solo is that such people may never get those automatic brain functions, which is the whole point of developing the lower centers of the brain. Such people may then incorrectly conclude that developing the lower brain does not yield lasting, remarkable results. That's why some initial guidance can go a long way toward ensuring that this development progresses as intended and that people do reap the benefits of having those highways.

WHAT'S NEXT

You are about to begin the last part of this book, in which you will learn many specific ways to restore your nervous system's flexibility. As you do so, you'll discover that the cumulative effect of implementing *all three parts* of the nervous system's trifecta is what makes an easier life a reality for all of us.

PART 3

The Nervous System's Trifecta: Getting Started Right Now

10

RESTORING OUR NERVOUS SYSTEM'S FLEXIBILITY: THE BASICS

Maybe we've just wrapped up a relaxing yoga class, an invigorating run, or a peaceful meditation. And then this happens: Feeling refreshed and rejuvenated, we check our phone. And there it is—that one text that shifts us into protection mode. And within less than a second, all our prior calmness is gone.

But here's the problem. It's not as though we can walk into another yoga class, go for another five-mile run, or do another 20-minute meditation. So, while replenishing our nervous system is important, it is only one of three components that keep our nervous system flexible and nourished.

We also need a myriad of simple approaches to do in the moment to resolve a current perceived threat. For example, while that text was concerning, *there was no attacking tiger.* That's why we now need to do an automated calming action that we've previously practiced while in connection mode. Such practice makes it possible for our nervous system to interpret whichever action we choose as "Got it. False alarm. I am safe." That's what the resolving component of the nervous system does for us. It quickly gets us back to connection mode when there's no true immediate danger.

Yet this is a trifecta approach. That means we do not just resolve and replenish. We also need to repair our nervous system's landscape. This is when we address whatever is creating ongoing stress and keeping our nervous system in high alert. If we skip over this part, it will seem as though we are always resolving threats and that we're never truly feeling replenished. However, when we address all three components—resolving, repairing, and replenishing—we end up with a flexible, resilient nervous system.

IF WE FORGOT TO ASK

Imagine the following scenario.

> A technician is installing a house alarm in Ming's home. Since Ming knows that such alarms go off even when there is no real danger, she asks the technician, "How do I deactivate a false alarm?"
>
> The tech shakes his head. "Sorry, there's no way to turn off this alarm."

What? Of course, none of us would ever install an alarm like that. And yet, while we've accepted that our bodies have a built-in stress alarm that sounds at the slightest hint of potential danger, we may have never asked that same question: How do I quickly turn off those false alarms?

While that answer has yet to hit prime time, here is the good news: Our body does have natural ways to counter those false stress alarms. That makes sense, since our physiology is always striving for stability.

THE BODY'S RESPONSE

As part of our stress reaction, our body always braces for the impending threat. That's why it helps to become aware of exactly *how* our body tells us that the alarm has already sounded. After all, the sooner we recognize that we've shifted into protection mode, the more quickly we can prevent that reaction from escalating. Most importantly, we can begin to resolve the threat.

Okay, some of you may be thinking, "Body bracing? What is she talking about?" And that's a fair question. When we ask Brain Highways participants how their body braces once in protection mode, some of them are also initially perplexed by the question. However, just hearing that question catches their brain's attention to become mindful of their body the next time they are upset.

But many participants, including the kids, already seem to know what their body does, noting that we don't all brace in the same way. For example, participants often share that they have experienced sensations such as a tightening in their throat or chest, back pain, and tingling on their face. For me, I know that my body has braced for a threat whenever I feel unexpected pain in my upper right shoulder (yes, it's that specific, meaning that my left shoulder never seems affected) or when I experience a tightening at the top of my diaphragm. At times, it's wild—I can be thinking that nothing stressful has even happened, and yet, seemingly out of nowhere, my right shoulder starts to hurt, or I experience that feeling in my diaphragm.

For example, just the other day, my daughter was telling me what she had heard about someone who I haven't seen or talked to in over six years. But almost immediately, there it was. As she was talking, I could feel that pain in my right shoulder. Clearly, my nervous system found something alarming about what my daughter was saying.

To note, we don't always have to know *why* we've shifted into protection mode when we realize that our body has braced for a perceived threat. We can still just go straight to doing one or more calming actions. In fact, we are more likely to figure out what truly triggered us *after* we're back in connection mode than when we rely on whatever explanation our cortex concocts while we are still feeling threatened.

There is another reason it helps to become aware of our body's bracing reaction. This awareness can also become our reference point for knowing whether our body now believes an original threat *has been resolved*. In other words, has that body-bracing sensation passed, or is it at least less intense after we engaged in one or more calming actions? That answer can then guide us to know whether we may need to do a calming action a bit longer or decide to engage in several more calming actions. Differentiating small and significant nuances in how our body changes for when we're in both protection and connection mode is always going to be part of restoring our nervous system's flexibility.

Our body's posture may also give us clues about what is going on in our nervous system. For example, how do we react when we hear a loud unidentified sound coming from behind us? We instinctively hunker down, round our shoulders, and drop our head. So, while it's possible that our everyday, normally rounded shoulders and slightly dropped head posture is just the result of sitting too long in front of a computer, what if part (or all) of that posture is coming from our subconscious mind, which still thinks there's an ongoing threat?

Or what if we notice that our posture is good most of the time, but that's how our body changes whenever we start to dorsal dive. If so, such awareness is helpful if we now view that shift in posture as a signal to *somehow move* to prevent further shutdown and dissociation.

To note, there's an entire approach called somatic experiencing, which was created by Peter Levine, a psychologist, researcher, and decades-long pioneer in the field of neurobiology. When doing the somatic experiencing method, trained professionals help people become curious as to how and where their body may still be living with and responding to a prior stressful event. Such professionals then guide people to release whatever motor patterns have become trapped to finally complete their body's original stress reaction. Watching Peter Levine demonstrate this approach with someone who has been struggling for years is compelling. Our nervous system and bodies are clearly intertwined in many ways.

HOW WE END UP WITH AUTOMATED STRESS REACTIONS

Whenever we don't have to think about whatever we are doing, then we've already automated that action. For the most part, automation is a phenomenal feature of our brain. After all, if we had to think about *everything*, we would be exhausted and never get anything done. However, automation is not so great when our brain automates protective-mode reactions that cause us to continually disconnect from others.

From a brain's perspective, automated stress reaction pathways will always be its favorite go-to whenever we're triggered. For starters, if an action is already automated, it will require little energy to do (and the brain is all about conserving energy when we're threatened).

But then, how do we automate a stress reaction in the first place?

Well, maybe we yelled at someone *who then backed down or gave us what we wanted.* If so, our brain went, "Great! That worked well." In such a case, our brain processed yelling as a useful "power over" response. Power-over protection-mode responses (which include far more than just yelling) are intended to have the same effect as when we raise our arms and make loud noises if we suddenly encounter a bear. Those defensive moves are supposed to make the bear believe

that we are *so big* that we can overpower it—which should then convince the bear to back off and leave us alone.

And that's why the next time we feel stressed, we're going to yell
once more, and then again and again. Apparently, our brain doesn't
seem to mind if our automated stress reactions do not work *all the
time*. For example, perhaps we get what we want by yelling just two
out of ten times. Yet, to our brain, those are good-enough odds to
keep doing that stress reaction. But at one point, we will have yelled
enough times (or will have done whatever protection-mode reaction
we engage in once triggered) that the status of those pathways has
now changed to being an *automated circuit*.

HOW WE DISABLE AUTOMATED
STRESS REACTIONS

The first step in disabling our stress reactions is to identify what
we've already automated. While some reactions are obvious, others
may be more subtle. For example, engaging in negative self-talk, a
penchant for perfectionism, a need to "fix" whatever is wrong, and
being critical of others are just a few examples of less-blatant automated stress reactions.

However, the process for disabling both overt and subtle stress
reactions is always the same. First, we need to stop traveling down
those prior automated highways. The commonly known adage about
the brain—"Use it or lose it"—is spot on here. That's because the
fewer times our automated stress reactions highways are activated,
the sooner they will lose their high-ranking status.

Yet it's unlikely that we can just say, "Stop it" (as in "Stop doing
that automated stress response!") and suddenly no longer engage in
such actions. If we could just tell our brain to stop doing something,
no one would be addicted to anything. We would just say, "Stop
drinking" or "Stop smoking" or "Stop gambling," and that would

be it. Disabling our automated stress circuitry requires much more than shutting down those pathways. We also need to automate new, helpful ways to respond. Otherwise, our brain will quickly revert to what it already knows when we are stressed.

As a heads-up, while disabling automated stress reactions is certainly doable, it can be challenging. For starters, we all have a stacked deck against us.

Think about it: Most of us have engaged in our prior automated stress reactions at least 5,000 or more times, as compared to maybe doing a calming action a handful of times. With those kinds of odds, which reaction do you think we'll likely do once triggered? Until we also automate new responses that return us to connection mode, we will not level this playing field.

Here is a simple way to view this process: Imagine a scoreboard with two competing teams, Protection Mode and Connection Mode. In this competition, every time we do one of our prior automated responses, the Protection Mode team scores a point. Every time we respond in a way that keeps us grounded, the Connection Mode team scores a point. Well, if Protection Mode keeps running up the score, then we're never going to change our landscape. Yet if we choose to *do something different*—right when we're about to react with our prior automated stress reaction—we keep our protection mode score low, while our connection mode score goes up.

THE POTENTIAL ROADBLOCK

A reliable, resilient, flexible nervous system is always the endgame. In Chapters 11 to 13, I offer specific ways to resolve, repair, and replenish the nervous system so that you can start to enhance or restore your own nervous system's flexibility. Yet I intentionally chose to present this chapter first. Before you embark on this journey, I want to give you some nervous system basics. But I also bring to your attention a potential roadblock that might inadvertently prevent you from moving forward.

This roadblock can be summed up with a five-letter word: *proof.* Considering the nervous system's tendency to be overly cautious, it should come as no surprise that we want assurance (especially when engaging in something new) that whatever we may consider trying has already been proven to work.

Yet in today's world, it can be challenging to know what brain and nervous system approaches are valid or not. That's because social media and the internet make it so easy for anyone to write anything. Whereas some people might say a program is miraculous, others will ping it as pseudoscience with no merit whatsoever. However, we don't have to unanimously agree on what is helpful or not. The following analogy offers a way for people with differing views to coexist and stay in connection mode.

Imagine a two-lane highway that represents all the possible calming approaches in the world. The left lane has only those approaches that meet gold-standard-research criteria; the right lane has everything else.

Traditionally, most people start in the left lane. But after a while, some people decide that it's time to make a lane change; they are now curious about what appears in the right lane. It's not that these people no longer believe in the scientific validity of what's being offered in the left lane. Rather, it may be as simple as that some of those left-lane approaches are not affordable or accessible in that person's community. Or perhaps they *have* tried some of those approaches, but they did not yield the kind of results they personally had hoped would happen.

Since this highway is big enough for both lanes to coexist side by side, for the most part everyone cruises along in their lane. Each driver is respectful of the other drivers on the road—even if some are traveling in a lane that differs from the one they've chosen for themselves. There's also nothing that stops people from changing lanes as often as they like; they may switch over to one lane for some decisions but then cross back over into the other lane for different situations. That's the beauty of an open two-lane highway—we can choose our lane.

A RISK-FREE LANE CHANGE

When deciding which calming approaches to include in the Brain Highways program, I didn't limit myself to only those supported by gold-standard research. Yet as I ventured into the right lane, I purposely avoided any approach that seemed somewhat (or very) sketchy, or had what I thought was a risky downside, or made claims that I believed were in direct conflict with what I had already learned and experienced.

To help me specifically decide which right-lane approaches were in or out, I first came up with some simple statements to start the review process. I needed to make sure that each statement was congruent with whichever approach I was considering. If you're ever pondering a lane change, you may also find these statements helpful when deciding what resonates with you. Here is what needs to be true for me:

- The approach is something we can do on our own, meaning that we don't need anything more than ourselves to implement it.

- The approach parallels or has some similarity to what we've already experienced and might innately do when stressed.

- The approach has no adverse effect.

- The approach does not require us to stop anything that already benefits us, such as taking medication or seeking professional help.

- The approach has a plausible explanation, per our biology, as to why it calms our nervous system—or in the case of lower brain development, a plausible explanation as to how the movement relates to creating lower brain neural circuits.

Before I ever give a calming action a whirl, those are always my initial boxes to check. If I can check off all five, then I try the approach *multiple times*, since I know that our nervous system is inclined to reserve its enthusiasm for anything new. And then I ask this question: Does this calming action bring about any notable, helpful change in how I feel?

And, yes, I know my answer to that question is always 100 percent subjective. But subjectivity *is* the point when it comes to the nervous system.

WHY THE NERVOUS SYSTEM'S VIEW MATTERS THE MOST

Recall that my nervous system never cares about anyone or anything else. *It is always just about me.* My nervous system is also indifferent to logic and facts and is about as tunnel vision as it gets when it comes to what it considers valid information when making its assessments.

That means you can rattle off hundreds of gold-standard research studies, but if the targeted approach doesn't make *me* feel better, there will still be no buy-in from my nervous system. In the same way, my nervous system does not care if there isn't a single study that proves an approach's effectiveness if I feel calmer after doing certain actions.

And, of course, everyone else's nervous system works in that same exact way.

To be clear, I'm not dismissing the need for research. I'm just proposing that we do not have to wait to move forward until such research is conducted, especially if we're choosing approaches that are simple, without risk, and return us to connection mode.

The good news is that as more people become interested in living their life primarily in connection mode, it may become more the norm to merge both personal experiences *and* accepted research to prove that various calming and grounding approaches are effective. For example, over the past decades, mindfulness and meditation classes have gone from being in the right lane to having mostly mainstream acceptance. Today, even many medical insurance companies cover the cost of such classes.

As part of that transformation, who would have imagined that Buddhist monks and medical science would have joined together to scientifically prove that the brain responds very differently when we quiet our mind? Yet it was the Buddhist monks, already known to be masterful meditators, who agreed to have their brain imaged while they were in deep meditation.

Of course, the monks themselves did not need any studies to convince them of what they had already experienced firsthand and knew to be true. But the results of those studies more than likely opened the door for many more people to also accept and therefore experience the calming effects of meditation. It's worth noting that whatever starts out in the right lane can sometimes (slowly) cross over to the left lane.

WHEN OUR PROFESSION GETS IN THE WAY

My husband has a degree in marine biology and (recall) a master's degree in scientific instrumentation. In the early days of Brain Highways, Jim's educational background, work experience, and natural way of thinking prompted him to express a lot of skepticism about what I was doing. Of course, Jim wasn't trying to be unsupportive of my program. It was just that Brain Highways greatly conflicted with what he viewed to be substantiated scientific proof that something truly worked. However, I didn't mind that Jim challenged me. After all, I figured that his thoughts likely reflected what others also thought about what I was doing, and it wasn't as though his comments ever deterred me from continuing.

But during this time, I wasn't just sharing with Jim the various approaches I was trying out. I was also regularly sharing the amazing results we were observing time and time again. And then, at one point, I heard Jim talking to someone about Brain Highways in a way that sounded as though he no longer doubted that this unscientifically proven program worked.

I later asked him what had changed. His answer was simple. He said the sheer numbers of people who were experiencing significant positive changes made it impossible to ignore that something was happening—even if it had not yet been proven by gold-standard science.

Over the years, we've had many Brain Highways parents who have also worked in professions that by default prompted them to have initial skepticism about a program not supported by gold-standard research. Why then did these parents even enroll their child? Well, my experience has been that a parent's desire to help their struggling child often overrides a conflicting belief.

Probably one of my favorite stories underscoring that point was the neurosurgeon who facilitated Brain Highways with his daughter mostly in their home. She had been diagnosed with autism and was nonverbal at the time she started our program. But this neurosurgeon also drove two hours every week so that his six-year-old daughter could additionally participate in an on-site class at the Brain Highways Center. Over the span of that course, it seemed as though we replayed this same scene numerous times whenever he was on-site.

The neurosurgeon is standing next to me. His daughter has just said hi to me as she comes through the door. Yes, she is starting to speak. She is now happily smiling as staff guide her on some of our fun apparatus.

But the neurosurgeon has the same bewildered look on his face that I've seen before. (At this point, I pretty much know what's coming next.) He is now shaking his head as he says, "Nothing—absolutely nothing—in my training or work experience supports or validates what you are doing here."

He is not trying to be combative. He is truly just stating aloud how he thinks as a neurosurgeon.

But then, he shifts to how he thinks as a parent, which is where these exchanges always end. The bewildered expression is now replaced with a beaming smile as he says, "So, no, I really do not get what you are doing—*but thank you!*"

PLACEBOS, BABIES, AND DOGS

If we are already biased to believe that an approach has no merit, then we often feel compelled to come up with a plausible explanation when others claim (or even insist) that they did feel better while or after doing that approach. In such cases, those with a bias will often say, "Okay, maybe someone did feel calmer, but that's only because the person experienced a placebo effect—not because there was any validity to that approach."

First, even if that were true, how did it come to be that many people associate a placebo as something negative, as in the brain was somehow duped into thinking that something works? To me, it's always *great news* if by just believing something, we can create and experience a positive change.

Second, the placebo-effect explanation never flies when people observe others doing these same calming approaches with *babies and dogs*. After all, babies and dogs have no prior knowledge that an approach is supposed to calm them. And so people cannot deny what they observe: Almost on cue, the crying baby stops wailing. The overly excited dog is suddenly calm. To remove any doubt that babies and dogs will react this way, we have captured some of those remarkable responses on video so that we can share such footage with our Brain Highways participants.

BUDDY

My 75-pound golden retriever, Buddy, stars in one of those calming videos. While Buddy is great, he does go from being a mellow dog to an over-the-top excited dog whenever someone enters our house. While that amped, excited state doesn't last more than a few minutes, it's quite annoying. Buddy will start doing a series of jumps right in front of the person (as though he just wants to see that person's face), which is not appreciated by even the biggest dog lovers.

Repeated dog training sessions did not end this behavior. That was because, in my interpretation, once Buddy was so excited, he couldn't remember whatever he had learned. We eventually decided to use the same building-into-the-structure approach that we do at Brain Highways. Since we could predict what Buddy would do when visitors arrived, we could also preempt that, right? So this is what we've been doing for years: Before a visitor enters our house, we ask Buddy, "Where is your toy?" And he will quickly run to get one.

As soon as Buddy starts chomping on that toy, he receives some calming proprioceptive stimuli. Although we still hear loud, excited doggy moaning as Buddy runs a lap or two around our living room, the toy in his mouth effectively prevents him from jumping when the person comes inside. And like I said, his excitement never lasts more than a few minutes before he's back to just lying down (all on his own), as though he had never been in high gear.

However, occasionally someone comes inside our house *before* we've had a chance to ask that question—and there is no toy in sight. That's when I resort to doing a calming tapping approach on Buddy that I've done with him since he was very young. The immediate difference in Buddy always amazes whoever has just arrived and witnesses the transformation.

Of course, this is key and not likely known to whoever is observing: That approach is something Buddy has already experienced, again and again, *when he wasn't in an excited state*. In other words, his brain has already automated that kind of touch as calming and relaxing.

But then this happened, which surprised even me.

It is the Fourth of July. In prior years, Buddy has never been bothered by firecrackers, which is consistent with the fact that he's also not bothered by thunder or other notably loud sounds.

Buddy is camped out on his bed when an extremely loud firecracker goes off right outside our home. For whatever reason, Buddy reacts and starts panting quite heavily. But since he has no history of loud noises making him anxious, Jim just gives Buddy a pat on the back and assures him that he's fine. While this is happening, I'm sitting at the kitchen table. However, I can see that Jim's quick assurance has not registered with Buddy because he's still acting agitated.

Buddy now runs over to me. Since I want to finish what I'm presently eating, I tell Jim to call him back over to him. However, Buddy will not go to Jim. This is also odd because we are both equal owners of our dog. And Jim is even the one who feeds Buddy (and to a golden retriever, food is everything!).

Not only is Buddy still panting heavily, but he's now trying to climb up onto my lap—and he has also never done that before. No matter how many times Jim tries to call him back to where he is seated, Buddy ignores him. He will not leave me.

Then a strange thought pops into my mind. Is Buddy somehow

asking me to do the calming tapping approach on him? Is this why
he won't go to Jim, who has never done that with him?

I figure I have nothing to lose as I start doing the same approach
that I've done with Buddy for years. Not surprisingly—since Buddy
is extremely anxious, as compared to his short-term, new-person-
at-the-door excitement—it takes me a full 10 minutes before his
panting starts to slow down. But the approach is clearly helping.
Another 10 minutes, and Buddy is back to his old self.

You will never convince me that this specific kind of touch does
not calm Buddy. But, granted, the part about Buddy *asking* me to
do this approach on him—well, I admit that's a bit sketchy. So I will
give you any eye rolling you choose to do for that part of the story.

But this is my point: Like the rest of us, dogs (and babies) also
have a nervous system that gets triggered *and* can be calmed by a
simple, specific kind of touch.

WE NEED TO DO ALL THREE

Maybe we are discouraged because we've already tried approaches to
help our nervous system but we still do not feel peaceful or calm. But
maybe we didn't address each of the three parts of this trifecta. To
have a flexible, resilient nervous system, we need to resolve threats in
real time, repair our landscape, and replenish daily. Doing just one
or two of the three will not cut it any more than we might expect
our car to run well if we put oil in the engine and air in our tires but
glossed over putting gas in the tank.

However, if we haven't yet done all three parts, here's why I would
say that is good news: Like the car without gas in the tank, we can now
do whatever we originally overlooked—and move forward from there.

11

FAST WAYS BACK TO CONNECTION MODE

How many attacking tigers did you come across this week? How about last month? Last year? Unless you were on a safari or engaged in some bizarre situation that included an angry tiger, your answer is going to be none. And yet your stress alarm probably sounded multiple times, or maybe even round-the-clock throughout the week.

However, recall that our nervous system's risk assessment is wrong—like almost all the time. So we need to be skilled at turning off our stress alarm whenever there is no true danger. That way, we quickly stop our brain's pharmacy from sending more stress hormones into our body. At the same time, we're also sending an important message to our brain and nervous system that we *have* effectively resolved the threat. We are safe.

But just as we cannot expect everything to go well if we show up for a sports tournament or music recital without practicing, the same applies when doing calming approaches after we're triggered.

Unless we have first practiced these approaches again and again *while in connection mode*, they will not be helpful.

To underscore the importance of that point, imagine that each of us has a nervous system bank account. Every time we practice a calming action in connection mode, we're making a deposit into that account. That way, we never find ourselves in stressful situations, trying to make a withdrawal from an empty account.

Fortunately, there are many ways to turn off our internal stress alarm. But for this chapter, I chose to share examples that are easy to understand (without watching a video demonstration), popular among Brain Highways participants, and effective for returning to connection mode in real time. In most cases, I also include how we've added our own spin to common techniques.

FUN WITH DEEP BELLY BREATHING

Shallow breathing means danger, and deep breathing means that we're safe. Deep belly breathing is like texting our brain, "You can turn off the stress alarm."

But we discovered that many of our Brain Highways participants, including adults, had never really learned how to do deep belly breathing. So we expanded on a balloon visualization that's sometimes used to help people picture deep breathing. Those original instructions tell people to imagine that they are inflating a balloon as the stomach rises on the inhale and then deflating that balloon as the stomach goes back down on the exhale. In our family program, we also include some tactile and visual stimuli as everyone pictures that balloon. We start by having the parents lie on their back. The kids are seated on the floor, right near the middle of their parent's body, as they place their hand on top of their parent's belly. That way, the kids can *see* their own hand rise and fall as their parent inflates and deflates "the balloon," as well as *feel* those changes. The parents and kids then switch roles.

To have fun practicing deep breathing while in connection mode, our family program participants also do the Book Breathing Challenge. Here, the child lies on the floor, on their back. The parent, who is seated right by their child, is also near a stack of books. Parents start the challenge by placing the first book on top of their child's belly. Without using any hands to help balance the book, the child takes a deep belly breath and tries to keep the book from falling off. If the book stays on, the parent places another book on top of that. The child now tries to keep both books balanced while taking another deep belly breath. The idea is to see how many books the child can balance until they all come tumbling down. (You'd be surprised how many books kids can stack for this challenge!)

We also added our own bit of fun when doing something called Hot Chocolate Breathing. In the traditional version, people imagine that they are holding a hot cup of cocoa. On the inhale, they pretend to smell its enticing aroma. But since the imagined cocoa is too hot, they must now exhale to try to cool it down. But in our spin, we deleted the too-hot part, and we changed the first part of this approach to be more of a tantalizing tease of when participants will finally be able to take a sip. Our version goes like this:

Imagine you're holding a cup with some delicious hot chocolate. Raise your cup toward your nose as you inhale and breathe in its delicious aroma. Now as you exhale, go, "Ahhhhhhhh," just thinking how great this cocoa is going to taste.

But wait! Before you take a sip, let's add some marshmallows. So put a few marshmallows into your hot chocolate. Raise your cup, and once again, inhale to breathe in its delicious aroma, and exhale as you go, "Ahhhhhhhh."

Wait! Before you take a sip, let's crush some Oreos and sprinkle that on top.

We continue adding more and more ingredients to the hot

chocolate (whipped cream, cinnamon, a candy cane to stir every-thing). Each time everyone inhales to get a good whiff of the enticing aroma and then exhales an anticipatory "Ahhhhh"—only to learn that it's still not time to take a sip. When everyone finally gets to drink the imaginary cocoa, we end our Hot Chocolate Breathing by exhaling one long "Mmmmmmmmmmm."

In truth, we created this more playful approach for the kids but quickly learned that parents in our family program love Hot Chocolate Breathing just as much as their kids do. So we added it to our adult-only program, and—go figure—Hot Chocolate Breathing is a hit with those participants as well.

Of course, the internet is full of deep breathing examples, so I don't feel the need to share more ways to do this. But whenever you find approaches that resonate with you, I encourage you to liven up a few of those. The more ways that deep belly breathing can be entertaining while in connection mode, the more likely people (especially kids) will practice doing this effective way to tell our nervous system that we are okay.

VOOING

On an inconsequential day, I came across a video that encouraged people to "voo" (rhymes with "boo") as a way to calm their nervous system. Now, if Peter Levine wasn't the person modeling this, I'm not sure I would have kept watching. But recall that Peter Levine is the creator of the somatic experiencing method. I've also always liked the way he comes across in his books and video interviews. He is clearly knowledgeable, authentic, and undoubtably sincere in his desire to help others.

So there was Peter Levine inhaling, and then on the exhale he let out a long v-o-o-o-o (coming from deep down in the belly) that resembled more or less the sound of a foghorn. He looked so earnest when he was doing this, like vooing was the most natural thing ever. But I was thinking, "Okay, how am I going to ever get Brain Highways participants, especially the teens and dads, to voo—and with the same kind of straight face that Peter Levine was modeling?"

But again, because this was Peter Levine, I decided to find out why vooing would be helpful. I discovered that the vibrational part of this approach, which comes from the voo sound, has to do with our vagus nerve. It turns out that our vagus nerve is very involved in our stress reaction, and it sends a lot of information to our brain. That interested me.

Yet I'm still shaking my head as I imagine myself vooing in front of a Brain Highways class, with everyone just staring back at me like I've completely lost it. However, I put that thought on hold because I haven't even tried to voo. Maybe this approach won't find its way into the Brain Highways program. After all, part of my criteria is that I first practice whatever I consider including in our courses.

And that's why I started to voo at various times when I was in connection mode. Full disclosure, though: Even after doing it for a while, I was probably more indifferent than enthused about vooing.

And then this happened.

I'm driving to the Brain Highways Center, but I'm now stopped at one of those long four-way traffic signals, having just missed my turn to go. I know that I'm going to be here for a while. And that's when I start to feel the beginning of a leg cramp! I immediately go into protection mode.

My prior experiences with leg cramps have only been at night when I didn't drink enough water during the day. Those leg cramp experiences were like 20 minutes of excruciating pain, with frenzied attempts to find a way to move to end the cramping.

Of course, I'm panicking, since this is happening right now *in the car*, where there is no way I can get up and move to stretch my leg. And how am I supposed to drive with my leg cramping? "Okay," I think, "I'll just pull over as soon as the light turns green to at least get out of the car to stretch this leg." But it's the first day of a session, and I'll most certainly mess everyone up if I'm 20 minutes late. Meanwhile, the pain is increasing.

That's when I decide to voo, right there and then. I get in three good, long voos before the light changes. It's now my turn to go.

As I'm turning left, I do yet another vigorous voo (I'm desperate), and I realize that the pain is starting to subside! Very encouraged, I voo once again as I continue to drive, and I'm now shocked. Literally stunned. The leg cramp is gone! Apparently, my nervous system resonates with vooing when I am in protection mode.

That experience certainly motivated me to bring vooing to the Brain Highways participants. However, while vooing and I have now become best buds, nothing about its weirdness has changed. That's why I always present vooing to our participants with this introduction.

First, I call it like it is. I am up front as I share, "No one looks cool when vooing. I'm not even going to try to spin that as a possibility. Yet when we're in protection mode, it's never about what *we* think is cool. It is only about what calms our nervous system. And it turns out, vooing is exactly what many nervous systems really like."

But at Brain Highways, we also make it fun to practice vooing while in connection mode. For example, we have vooing contests. Whether at home or in a class, everyone (all at the same time) inhales and then voos on the exhale, trying to be the last person still vooing before taking a new breath.

Parents of babies have also become big fans of vooing if they discover that their baby's nervous system is responsive to it. (Parents of a crying baby will overlook weirdness much more easily if something stops their baby from wailing.)

Here, parents voo while they hold their baby against their chest since that allows their little one to additionally feel the vibration generated from the vooing. Or they can voo right near their baby's ear, creating white noise, which additionally calms a baby. Mirror neurons are also at play here, meaning that if the vooing calms the parent, then the baby's nervous system will also pick up on that and respond accordingly.

Well, I have now been vooing for close to five years. I can't really say that it seems any less weird, but hands down, vooing ranks as one of my top three ways that I can quickly calm my nervous system, and I hear similar rankings among Brain Highways participants.

TAPPING

When we feel anxious, some people may automatically start tapping their fingers on a desk or their foot on the floor. However, with the emotional freedom technique (EFT), people tap on nine specific parts of our body.

Dr. George Goodheart, Dr. Roger Callahan, and Gary Craig are generally credited as the initial forerunners of EFT. However, the Ortner family (Nick, Jessica, Alex, and Karen) probably put tapping "on the map" with their best-selling books and world tapping summits. The Ortners' nonprofit tapping foundation has also helped many people, such as families after the tragic Sandy Hook shooting, survivors of genocide in Rwanda, and veterans with PTSD.

First, as a full disclaimer, I have never presented EFT to Brain Highways participants by its official name. But that decision is not out of any disrespect. I readily acknowledge how millions of people worldwide have benefited from the emotional freedom technique. I was just concerned that I'd lose a lot of our participants from the get-go, probably right after the word "emotional," if I introduced a calming action as the emotional freedom technique. Simply calling it tapping (which others do as well) seemed like a better fit for the Brain Highways participants.

I have also strayed from the more traditional formatted tapping scripts used in EFT videos and apps that begin with what's called a set-up statement related to a specific topic. Here, people follow whoever is leading that routine as they are guided where to tap on each point while listening (and sometimes repeating) the corresponding script. Again, that format works well for many people.

But within the context of our program, I wanted everyone, especially the kids, to believe that they could tap all on their own right from the get-go. That way, it would be easier and more likely for them to use this approach in real time as situations came up throughout the day. However, even with our more simplified approach, we do use the same traditional nine tapping points. (I've included where each of those points are in Appendix D.)

Our participants are introduced to tapping by first deciding how they would like to feel (at that moment) from what we call nine superpower highways: acceptance, compassion, courage, curiosity, gratitude, harmony, joy, kindness, and peace.

They then follow this short script (that intentionally has few words to remember) while tapping on those nine points. For example, if I wanted to feel peace rather than yell at my kids to stop fighting, I could now tap on those specific points while saying (to myself or aloud), "I choose peace. Peace is my power. Peace. Peace. Peace. I choose peace." To note, there is no established number of times to tap through all nine points before we feel calmer. But if we've already shifted into protection mode, just one or two rounds will not usually be enough to return to connection mode.

Once participants feel more grounded, they wrap up this first part by reminding their brain of something quite important. So I would finish tapping on peace by saying, "It does not matter how long it lasts. A minute. A morning. A month. I choose peace for this moment."

That focus is critical in terms of the bigger picture. When people first try any kind of calming action, they often mistakenly think that it will automatically have a lasting effect. And if it does not, they quickly conclude that the approach did not work. By doing this specific wrap-up, we remind ourselves (while still tapping) that we're focusing only on the present moment. Staying present is also a key concept when practicing mindfulness.

Once our participants have been doing this simplified way to tap, we introduce additional spin-off tapping approaches. Some of those even include an effective way to get a date stamp on those charged unresolved memories. (Those kinds of memories are introduced in Chapter 4.)

But while our various tapping formats differ from one another, one criterion remains the same: Participants can do any of these spin-offs all on their own. Of course, that independence doesn't preclude them from also seeking help from trained EFT professionals. In fact, participants often share that their positive Brain Highways tapping experiences are what gave them the confidence to dig deeper with a professional.

So where does tapping fall in terms of research? To date, over 100 research studies, review articles, and meta-analyses have been published in professional peer-reviewed journals. Among such studies are those showing that tapping reduces cortisol levels. Anything that reduces cortisol levels is always going to be a plus, since high levels of cortisol wreak havoc on both our body and nervous system.

At this point, tapping is not yet considered to be among those gold-standard research approaches, although the mounting evidence is making that a possibility in the very near future (or it may have already happened by the time you read this). However, the absence of that level of research has not deterred our participants (and clearly millions of people from all over the world) from embracing this simple way to get back to connection mode and to put date stamps on emotionally charged unresolved memories.

HAVENING

Another easy-to-use calming action is called havening. Dr. Ronald Ruden, the creator of this approach, named it havening in reference to finding a safe haven.

I first became interested in havening because it is based on touch. Even without research, we have all experienced touch as comforting. But we have also experienced how that very same touch—done by another person—might now feel creepy. We've additionally experienced touch as being too rough, even painful. So we already have a sense that touch can affect our nervous system.

The way we apply touch while doing the simple havening movements is supposed to produce delta brain waves. These are the low-frequency waves that ordinarily occur when we are deeply asleep or very relaxed, such as when meditating.

As is the case with many other calming approaches, I cannot say at this time that I have found absolute, universal confirmation that havening produces delta waves. However, I can share that I personally, as well as many of the Brain Highways participants, do feel much calmer after doing the havening movements for about 10 minutes. I can also share that my eight-month-old granddaughter stops crying—like, instantly—as soon as I start to do the havening movement on her face. Of course, there's zero downside to doing these three havening movements. Here's how they are done:

For the first havening movement, cross your arms and place one hand on your right shoulder and your other hand on your left shoulder. At the same time, use each hand to stroke down to your elbows. Return your hands to the top of each shoulder and repeat stroking your hands down to your elbows. Continue this same movement, going from the top of the shoulders to the elbow, again and again.

For the second havening movement, place your middle fingertips (on both hands) at the top of your forehead, and bring them down around the side of your face to your chin. Return your fingertips to the top of your forehead and continue this same motion, again and again. (You can also start under your eyes and go out and down to your chin.) For the third havening movement, just rub the palms of your hands back and forth, much like you would do when washing them.

Havening's flexibility and simplicity are what make this approach so easy to do. For example, we do not need to do these movements at a certain speed; we can go as fast or as slow as we find comforting. It also makes no difference whether we do the movements on top of a heavy sweatshirt or on our bare skin, whether we do all three movements, or (if we do all three) in what order we do them. It's equally optional whether we think or say something affirmational while doing the movements, whether we do them to ourselves, or whether someone does them to us.

Interestingly, we may have already naturally done one or more of these havening movements when we were stressed. In fact, just the other day, I was watching a television show where the mom was comforting her very upset adult daughter—and what was the mom doing? Continually stroking her daughter's arm from her shoulder to her elbow. (I was momentarily distracted as I thought, "Hey, she is havening!")

While there are many applications for these movements in the havening community, the Brain Highways program includes it as a simple calming tool whenever fear or anxiety or any other emotion seems to be getting in the way of moving forward. That's how my four-year-old grandson recently used havening.

This story begins when my grandson showed up to his first-ever soccer practice with a team that had already worked with this particular coach. Right away, the coach had all the kids scream at the top of their lungs to see if they could get him to fall over. (No, I don't know the rationale for starting soccer practice this way.)

That loud, unexpected, wild screaming blindsided my grandson. Over the next few days, he kept talking about the *very loud* screaming at soccer practice. But after role-playing some different calming actions that he might do at his next practice, my grandson seemed fine about returning. I was at his second practice, and so I saw firsthand what happened.

My grandson gets out of the car in the parking lot (which is right near the field) with every intention of walking over to the coach and the other kids. But as soon as he sets foot on the field—where he can now clearly see the coach and the other kids who are gathered around him—he temporarily freezes. The sight of them is enough for his nervous system to sound the alarm, commanding him *not* to move forward. After all, moving forward means getting closer to the danger!

Yet my grandson does not turn around and come back to his mom and me, where we are now getting situated to the side of the practice area. Instead, we see him stroking his hands down the side of his arms as he slowly steps toward his coach and teammates.

And because he is four, he doesn't care about how this looks (or perhaps he thinks that everyone does this), so he is now saying aloud for all to hear, "I am safe. I am calm. This will pass." ("This" referring to whatever emotion he feels at that moment.) He continues doing the havening movement from his shoulders to his elbows, saying those phrases as he keeps moving toward his team.

Once there, he never once looks back at us with a "Did you see what I just did?" expression. The kids now start their screaming, and we see my grandson do a few more havening movements as they do so—and that was that.

PROPRIOCEPTION (AGAIN)

In Chapter 8, I include ways to stimulate our proprioceptive system within the context of that chapter. There, the focus is on how proprioceptive movements can help those who haven't finished their lower brain development. But these same movements are also good for anyone who wants to stay grounded or shift back to connection mode. That's because it turns out that such stimuli have both an alerting and calming effect.

Riding roller coasters is one example of when we might intuitively stimulate our proprioceptive system when stressed. Think of barreling down a steep incline. What do many of us do? We reach over to the friend or family member seated next to us and *squeeze their hand* (while we also likely scream). Recall that squeezing is one of the ways we stimulate our proprioceptive system. As with tapping and havening, I always like when we innately calm ourselves without realizing there's a neurobiological basis for doing so. It just gives more credence to whatever someone else has claimed to be helpful.

In this chapter, I bring up proprioceptive movements, once again, for two reasons. I want to bring to your awareness the times you may already be calming yourself with proprioceptive movements. I also want you to know that anything I present in Chapter 8 can also be done when stressed.

CROSS-LATERAL MOVEMENT

Whenever we're rhythmically moving our opposite arm or leg, we are doing a cross-lateral movement. Walking, running, and swimming are examples of natural cross-lateral movement, and most people feel "better" after doing any of those three activities.

While there are theories on why cross-lateral movement is beneficial, none are proven by the gold standard of science. But the possibilities are interesting. They range from the theory that we are all hard-wired to find rhythm as something that calms us (starting from hearing the rhythmic heartbeat of our mother in utero) to the idea that this kind of movement brings back more blood flow (noting that blood flows *away* from our higher centers of the brain when we are in a fight, flight, or freeze reaction) to the theory that the movement helps integrate the left and right brain hemispheres (brain scans have shown that information is processed more efficiently when both sides of the brain are activated).

It's not always feasible to jump into a pool to swim laps or to go for a run or walk when we're triggered. However, any time we cross one hand over to the other side of our body, we have done a cross-lateral movement. Fortunately, there are lots of ways to alternate crossing each hand across our body, even while seated, to create a rhythm of cross-lateral movements. If we include squeezing or pressing as part of a crossover movement, then we have also added some proprioceptive stimuli. For example, we can slowly cross our right hand over to the top of our left arm to squeeze and release. We then slowly cross our left hand over to the top of our right arm to squeeze and release. We continue this way as we slowly inch down our entire arm until we are finally at our wrists and then work our way back up to the shoulders in the same way.

Or, when seated, we can cross over our right hand and press that palm firmly into our left thigh and then repeat that same movement with our left hand as we press on our right thigh. Once again, we continue with that cross-lateral rhythm and movement. While there is no set number of times to do any of these movements, the more times that we cross over, the more grounded we will likely feel.

But there is a gotcha to doing cross-lateral movements that I quickly discovered when I first introduced crossovers to my 16 students in those early days. I would tell them to follow along as I modeled crossing my right elbow over to touch my raised left knee (and vice versa). But when I would look out at the class, I would see the 16 putting their elbow on the same side—not the opposite side—of their body. Even stranger, they seemed to have no clue that they weren't crossing over like I was modeling.

It was not until I learned about the asymmetrical tonic neck reflex (ATNR) a few years later that I finally understood what I was observing back then. When that primitive reflex is retained—which is almost always the case when the lower brain development is not completed—it doesn't feel natural and automatic to cross the midline. And yet we need to easily cross the midline to do much more than crossover movements. Automatic midline crossing is also involved in reading, writing, playing certain sports, and much more.

THE MIDLINE WRAP

A particular calming and grounding position, often referred to as hook-ups or Cook's Hook-Up, has been around for decades. But at Brain Highways, we now call this the Midline Wrap. (The name change came after the *Urban Dictionary* and most people under 70 started attributing a more R-rated meaning to the phrase *hooking up*.)

I also taught this specific position to the 16. When they tried to do this while standing (the way I had been taught), they'd immediately start to wobble—some would even come close to falling over. I knew they weren't goofing around; rather, they just couldn't compensate for their poor balance when positioned that way. As soon as I had them sit instead of stand, that all changed. Without question, the position seemed to calm them. Today, at Brain Highways, we still have everyone do the Midline Wrap while seated on a chair.

To do the Midline Wrap, start by placing your feet on the floor, and then cross one foot over the other so that your ankles are crossed. Extend your arms in front of you, and now cross your right wrist on top of your left wrist (or vice versa, whichever feels the most comfortable). Turn your palms to face each other and interlace your fingers so that your hands are clasped. Now, bending your elbows, bring your arms a bit downward, and then turn them inward and upward so that your still-clasped hands are now resting on your chest. Place the tip of your tongue in the middle of the roof of your mouth—and then close your mouth. Shut your eyes and do some deep belly breathing.

To note, the reasoning offered for this body position and placement of the tongue centers around the idea that the person is completing an energy circuit generated, in part, from crossing the arms and ankles. The placement of the tongue is supposed to stimulate the limbic system, synchronizing emotional processing with the higher centers of the brain. While that all sounds lovely, I haven't found anything that supports any of that actually happening. Yet for over two decades, I myself have experienced and have observed thousands of people of all ages become notably calmer after remaining in this position for about five minutes. The simplest nonscientific explanation may be as follows.

When we are surging, we are not still. To the contrary, we're usually all over the place. In worst-case surging scenarios, we may use our hands to hurl objects or even hurt someone. Less extreme but still problematic, we can point a finger right in someone's face (or even use a finger to do an obscene gesture). Or we may use our legs to stomp and kick, which only makes the current situation even more inflammatory.

Yet when we are nicely contained in the Midline Wrap position, none of that is possible. And the tip of the tongue in the middle of the roof of the mouth? Well, it turns out that it's impossible to talk with the tongue positioned that way, which then becomes beneficial whenever people are upset. I have often said that we would all get out of protection mode much more quickly if we could not talk.

I GET YOU REPAIRS

We know that throwing water on a small fire can prevent those flames from spreading. In a similar way, an "I Get You Repair" effectively reduces a protection-mode surge from escalating. Whenever we can put the brakes on a surge, it is going to be much easier to return to connection mode.

Our version of an I Get You Repair is based loosely on Jennifer Kolari's CALM (connect, affect, listen, mirror) approach. However, our approach puts everything in the context of protection and connection mode. It's our understanding of the nervous system's primordial fear of getting kicked out of our pack that now guides us in terms of what to say when doing an I Get You Repair response. Recall that, to our nervous system, being all alone "on the savanna" is a huge threat to our survival, since, as humans, we are meant to be with other humans.

So whenever something in the present causes our nervous system to sound the alarm, right below the surface is always that unrelenting fear of being kicked out of our pack. That's why if people dismiss or judge (or even ridicule) how we are acting once in protection mode, that primordial fear is going to surface and add to the original threat. Those kinds of responses only escalate the protective-mode reaction. After all, if people do not understand us, or cannot relate to us, or disapprove of our actions—well, that just increases our chances of being left alone on the savanna.

Here is an example of when we might do an I Get You Repair: Suppose Noah is engrossed with his new video game as his mom enters the room and says, "Noah, turn off your video game. I have to get to the post office before it closes, and you need to come with me." But Noah ignores his mom and keeps playing. When his mother repeats her instruction, this time he shouts, "*I don't want to go!*"

If Noah's mom doesn't understand her son has shifted into

protection mode, she may shout back, "Turn it off *right now*—or you'll be grounded from video games for three days." Of course, her response to him reflects that she, too, has shifted into protection mode. With both of them in protection mode, their interactions will continue to go south.

Or if Noah's mom doesn't understand that logic and facts fly out the door once we are in protection mode, she might try to reason with him. Here, she might say, "Noah, I have to go *right now* because I need to make sure this package is in the mail today." Yet even with that calmer, rational response, it is unlikely that Noah will respond, "Oh, well, in that case, sure," and turn off the game. No, since Noah is already in protection mode, he now yells back, "I don't care if your stupid package gets mailed today!" And most likely, that package is never going to be sent that day, since both will continue to fling protective-mode responses at each other.

But here is where a quick I Get You Repair can make all the difference. Once again, suppose that Noah's mom has told him to turn off the video game so they can leave, and Noah shouts, "*I don't want to go!*" Only, this time, Noah's mom pauses, noting how her direction has shifted Noah into protection mode (as evidenced by his reaction). *She quickly imagines what Noah's nervous system needs to hear*—right at that moment—that validates his reaction. After all, his nervous system decided there was a potential threat and is not going to take kindly to being dismissed or judged for that assessment.

That's why Noah's mom now says, with the same indignation she imagines Noah's nervous system's tone would have if it could talk, "Wow, it's like I didn't even notice or care that you were in the middle of doing something that you love. And then I expected you to stop playing your new video game *right this second* to go somewhere you couldn't care less about going. That is *so* annoying!"

With those few sentences, Noah's mom has now validated why Noah's nervous system reacted the way it did. There is also the subconscious message that says, "I see you," which differs from the "I must be invisible" program that many kids end up downloading and carrying into adulthood. And, of course, there is the subconscious message that if his mom "gets" him, then he is safe, since he will now be staying with his pack.

However, Noah's mom's repair needs to be authentic, since Noah's nervous system will quickly detect any insincerity. But sounding sincere won't be difficult if Noah's mom realizes that she is not so different from her son. She, too, gets annoyed when people interrupt her (without warning) and expect her to do something right away with no regard to what she was already doing.

That's why this approach can seem so magical (as many Brain Highways parents exclaim). Upon hearing that nervous system validation, Noah is now just going to nod his head. That's it. That universal head nodding seems to be the nervous system's way of saying, "You do get me—so there's nothing more I need to say or any reason for me to double down."

From there, Noah and his mom can problem solve how to move forward for that situation and how to do things differently in the future. For example, Noah's mom might commit to giving him notice before ever telling him that he needs to stop playing his video game.

But what about when we shift into protection mode, and no one does an I Get You Repair *for us*? Well, that's when we just give our own nervous system an I Get You Repair. For example, suppose I overreacted when my teenage daughter was 10 minutes late. Again, to give my nervous system the validation it needs (which will help shift me back to connection mode), I might say something like, "Hey, I *get* why you sounded the alarm. Your assessment scan checked off the time my niece was late but was in a very serious accident!" And in the very same way that an I Get You Repair can temper someone else's reaction, that validation seems to assuage our own nervous system, thereby preventing us from surging even more.

TALKING TO YOUR NERVOUS SYSTEM

Yes, I am encouraging you to talk to your nervous system—and not only to validate its protective-mode reactions. We also want to make sure our nervous system knows that we *have survived* whatever threat it perceived might harm us.

In such cases, we want to keep repeating to our nervous system something such as, "I survived. We are good now. This event is *done*." It's even more effective if we are saying (or thinking) that dialogue while we are tapping, havening, positioned in the Midline Wrap, or doing any cross-lateral movement. That way, our entire brain gets the message. It is coming through when we are in a more relaxed, receptive state.

Okay, maybe talking to your nervous system sounds a little too out there for you. Yet today, there are many blog posts, podcasts, and books telling people to *befriend their nervous system*. Well, in my world, I don't expect people to be my friends—if I never talk to them.

A REALITY CHECK

If we try to pull out a calming action—for the first time ever—*after* we have shifted into protection mode, good luck. Our brain and nervous system are going to be like, "What are you doing?" Recall that for these actions to effectively calm and ground us, we need to first practice them, again and again and again, *while we are in connection mode.* There is just no getting around that truth.

But this is also true: We can become experts at returning to connection mode. However, if we don't also repair our nervous system's landscape, those ongoing stressors will continuously trigger our nervous system. In this case, it will be like we're right back in protection mode, again and again. That's why changing our nervous system's landscape, as needed, is also key to living a life in connection mode.

In the following chapter, you'll learn what may be keeping your nervous system on high alert (in addition to incomplete lower brain development) and specific ways to repair your nervous system's landscape.

12

~~~~~~~

REPAIRING THE LANDSCAPE

Suppose we know that our roof leaks in multiple places. Whenever it rains, we quickly gather buckets and strategically place them right where the water comes through. Of course, if we're not home when it rains, our carpet gets soaked, which then causes its own set of problems.

But since our roof leaks every time it rains, we should hardly be shocked when we once again run to get buckets or figure out a way to dry the carpet when it's soaked. After all, it's the same roof as the last time and every time before that whenever it rained.

Of course, *repairing* our roof, once and for all, would seem like a wise decision, right? Otherwise, it is going to be exhausting to keep coming up with temporary fixes that may not even always work. But then, wouldn't the same thinking hold true for repairing our nervous system—once and for all?

WHY WE CHANGE THE LANDSCAPE

We already know that a group of people can experience the very same event yet respond quite differently to what happened. For example, maybe nine soldiers are involved in a horrific surprise bomb explosion in Afghanistan, during which two soldiers die at the scene. Three of the surviving soldiers end up with post-traumatic stress disorder (PTSD), but the other four do not.

Several variables might explain why not all these soldiers have PTSD. But each soldier's nervous system—the degree of its flexibility and resilience at the time of the explosion—is never going to be inconsequential in terms of how each soldier deals with the aftermath.

Part of returning to a flexible nervous system is to make a concerted effort to clear whatever is presently making our personal landscape rocky and unstable. In other words, we want to show up on *solid ground* whenever life hits us with those unexpected hard challenges.

That's why when we repair our nervous system, we truly *change* our personal landscape. Yes, we want a vigilant nervous system (recall that part of its job is to be on the lookout for danger), but we do not want a *hypervigilant* nervous system that is *always* reacting as though we are going to be doomed within seconds. That's why this chapter presents what is often needed to repair our nervous system, along with specific ways that you can begin to repair your own nervous system—right now.

DO SOMETHING DIFFERENT (IN THE MOMENT)

Suppose I'm in a Broadway play, and night after night, I receive the same bad reviews. So one night I decide to change my lines, and I no longer say what I have been saying every night.

With my decision alone, it's a different play, right?

In our own lives, we may also find ourselves cast in the same play (that keeps getting poor reviews), in which everyone continues to repeat their inflammatory lines, which then puts everyone in protection mode. For example, suppose our teenage daughter has, once again, scattered her dirty clothes all around her room. Our typical response has been to yell, "Pick up your clothes and put them in the laundry basket *right now!*" Our daughter's typical response has been to either yell back or mutter some sarcastic comment.

But imagine that this time we enter her room with a sticky note on our forehead with this sole word on it: *Clothes.* This doesn't mean that our daughter instantly picks up her clothes. That's not why we do this (although wearing a sticky note with a friendly reminder will likely get a different response from her as well).

No, we do something different for one reason. We want to shut down those neural circuits that light up whenever we're in protection mode, the ones that reflect our *automated stress reactions.* Shutting down those pathways is key to repairing our nervous system. Here, we're never assessing whether doing something different "worked" by how someone else responds to what we did. It *always* works if we do something different because that means we did not activate our prior stress reaction. That is it.

Of course, putting sticky notes on our forehead is hardly the only way we can do something different. For example, maybe instead of nagging our child to take out the trash, we hold our nose and talk in a funny accent as we say, "I don't know who would want a smelly house," or we burst into a song about taking out the trash (the way people suddenly start to sing in musicals).

However, doing something different is not limited to goofy and playful responses. Suppose someone is not moving as quickly as we would like. Instead of saying, "Hurry up!" we now say, "How can I help you move forward?" Or when our child loses focus, instead of saying, "Pay attention," we might say, "Let's get up and move!" Or maybe we just give a hug instead of a lecture when our five-year-old accidentally knocks over the vase and it shatters into pieces on the floor. But what might be the simplest, most powerful way to do something different? We take a moment to pause—putting on hold whatever we might say or do next.

DO SOMETHING DIFFERENT (AS PREVENTION)

What about those predictable situations, the ones we know with certainty will trigger us? For example, my husband has this uncanny ability to fall asleep within 20 seconds after closing his eyes—and that's even if he is sitting up! However, Jim's falling asleep on speed dial became a problem in the evenings when I would talk to him while he was seated on the couch. I would see him close his eyes, but Jim would insist that he was still listening.

Yet he was clearly *not* listening because, like I said, he's in deep sleep in less than a minute once his eyes are closed. Predictably, I'd get triggered, which was why it was time to do something different.

I decide that I will no longer share information if Jim's eyes are not open. Although he assures me that he will now keep them open if I'm talking, he still sometimes closes them. I think it is a Pavlovian response for Jim, in which sitting on the couch in the evening signals to his brain, "Shut your eyes."

When this happens, I now stop midsentence—instead of waking him up like I used to do. Any doubt that Jim has drifted off is quelled by the fact that he never says, "Hey, why did you stop talking?"

But after this scenario recurs enough times, I do something different yet again. I know that when Jim is camped out on the couch in the evening, he is already tired, which is why I now no longer even bring up a topic to discuss with him at that time. It's just better to wait until the morning.

We can also apply doing something different whenever we can predict resistance. For example, there was the time I was talking with a Brain Highways parent and her 11-year-old son about his overt aversion to doing homework.

This 11-year-old is slumped over in his chair as the three of us are seated at a table. It is clear: The last thing he wants to talk about is *homework*.

But his mom is tired of all his daily resistance. She shares, "Just saying the word homework already puts him in protection mode."

I respond, "Then why not call it something else?" I turn to her son and ask, "What do you like? In other words, what makes you smile?"

I see him sit up a little, intrigued by where this conversation is unexpectedly going. He answers rather quickly, "Puppies."

"Okay, so why not call homework puppies?" I turn to his mom. "And now you just say, 'It's time for puppies!'"

They both start laughing.

I continue, "Of course, you would also do your puppy work somewhere completely different than before, in a new spot surrounded with photos of the cutest puppies ever."

They leave, excited to set up his new puppy workplace.

The beauty of doing something different is its simplicity. Yet it absolutely helps change our landscape.

I GET YOU REPAIRS FOR PAST SITUATIONS

Recall that our nervous system does not adhere to linear time. While its ability to time-travel to the past is not always helpful, we now take advantage of that feature when we do an I Get You Repair for times that we may have previously judged or dismissed someone's protective-mode reaction. In Chapter 11, you learned how to do an I Get You Repair as soon as someone shifted into protection mode. But now we're using that same approach to go back and remedy missed opportunities from the past as a way to help repair the nervous system.

In our Brain Highways program, parents often choose to do this kind of I Get You Repair with their child for past interactions that did not reflect an understanding of a lower brain connection. However, an I Get You Repair for the past is more than an apology, with a parent only saying something like, "I'm sorry that I didn't understand how you *were* really trying back then." Rather, in the same way that we do an I Get You Repair to validate someone's current reaction, the parent now imagines what their *child's nervous system* would have wanted to hear back then.

With that guideline, a Brain Highways parent might say, "It must have been *so frustrating* to hear me tell you—again and again—to try harder, sit still, and pay attention when you were already working so hard. Now I get why you would sometimes respond by becoming angry or shutting down. I just wouldn't stop harping on you. And yet how could you make any lasting changes if certain highways were not in place? I also get if you thought I was unfair to you, or maybe even thought that I didn't like you if you didn't act a certain way. I bet my own protective-mode reactions sometimes made you feel very lonely and isolated. I am so sorry that I didn't understand what was going on with your brain and nervous system—and that my brain made up stories to fill in those gaps."

Whereas kids most often respond to an I Get You Repair in real time with head nodding, they usually spontaneously embrace their parent after an I Get You Repair for the past. In both cases, such reactions reflect that the nervous system has truly "heard" what it wanted acknowledged.

That's why when we do an I Get You Repair for the past, it has a restorative, positive effect on someone else's nervous system.

Yet our own nervous system also benefits. For example, Brain Highways parents will often discover that this happens after doing an I Get You Repair for past interactions with their child. They will share that the experience ended up being surprisingly emotional (but in a positive way)—and just as much or more *for them* as for their child (while also noting that they may have even been the one who wanted to keep hugging).

SCARY MOVIES

While many people may not understand the physiology of fear in terms of what happens to our brain and nervous system, those who produce scary movies are very knowledgeable in this area. They expertly apply ways to trigger the brain's fear center when creating their scary movie.

That ensures that complete strangers (after all, it's not like they know who will be watching their movie) will feel frightened when seated in a movie theater or on a couch at home exactly whenever they want to sound our stress alarm. That also explains why we cannot fall asleep right after watching a really scary movie. Those same stress hormones are still circulating.

That's why even though we may think scary movies are fun entertainment, we may now decide to put such movies on hold while repairing our nervous system. After all, it's an easy action that helps keep our overall protection-mode score low.

Of course, once we've repaired our nervous system, we won't have the same need to stay away from such entertainment. Then again, with our newly repaired nervous system, we may discover that we now prefer a good comedy over a thriller.

TEXTS, SOCIAL MEDIA, AND THE NEWS

I'm not going to spend much time on how texts, social media, and the news affect our nervous system because I believe most (if not all of us) have already experienced being triggered by something we have just heard or read. Instead, I will share only a few thoughts to ponder.

First, our nervous system isn't naturally wired to connect with texts and social media posts. Instead, our nervous system needs to be interacting with real people, in real time. And while emojis have tried to fill in for the glaring absence of a real human's facial expression and tone of voice, I'm pretty sure that our nervous system would say this about emojis: "Nice try—but honestly, I am not wired to connect with a *visual representation of an emotion.*"

Second, headlines by design (in a similar way to scary movies) are intended to make us react. For example, if a headline triggers some fear, we are more likely to read the article or watch the video or listen to the podcast. And when scrolling through social media, we never really know what we will come across.

Again, it's all about the scoreboard. If we intentionally replace some of our time spent on social media with in-person opportunities to connect with a real human being (we go visit a friend instead of texting her), we increase our connection-mode score. And whenever we consciously reduce or eliminate our exposure to potential triggers, we, by default, are going to spend less time in protection mode. That's why both simple actions will always be helpful when repairing our nervous system.

THE ENVIRONMENTAL CONNECTION

Most people think they need to see mold growing on their bathroom walls or under their kitchen sink to even consider that mold may be adversely affecting them. Yet mold can also hide behind walls, inside air ducts, and in crawl spaces. That's important to know, since mold exposures can do numbers on some people's nervous system, wreaking havoc on both their memory and mood (in addition to adversely affecting their respiratory system and other parts of their body).

We also may not realize that pesticides—the ones commonly used inside and outside of our homes and offices—were originally derived from nerve gas in World War II. When we spray pesticides to get rid of kitchen ants or to kill weeds in our yard, we probably aren't thinking that we are inhaling neurotoxins or that neurotoxins are defined as substances that alter the structure or function of the nervous system. We're probably also unaware of the many other neurotoxins that have insinuated their way into our daily lives.

In a similar way, some people's biochemistry may be such that certain foods cause them to experience mood swings or to demonstrate aggressive behavior, even though those very same foods have no adverse effect on others. But, like mold and other possible environmental triggers, the connection between food and behavior is often overlooked. That's because those affected do not often have an immediate reaction (food stays in our digestive track for days) or their reactions are inconsistent (problematic foods can be tolerated if our overall stress level is low at the time we eat the food). Even a panic attack may have a connection to food. While there may be many reasons for a panic attack, low glucose levels could be playing a role in someone's anxiety.

Doctors who specialize in functional medicine rely on various tests to confirm or rule out whether environmental variables may be affecting someone's mental and physical health. If they are, these doctors can also present a variety of ways to remedy whatever may be causing an adverse effect.

NO-DATE-STAMPED MEMORIES
AND SUBCONSCIOUS PROGRAMS

While our conscious mind might be eager to dive in ("Okay, let's get that date stamp on all my charged memories! Let's change those subconscious programs that keep messing me up!"), our nervous system may not be on board. And that makes sense. Recall that our nervous system originally made the assessment to safeguard us from feeling emotional pain—and that it has been protecting us that way ever since. And so now what? After many years, even decades, at keeping those emotions below the surface, our nervous system is suddenly going to think it's safe to rock the boat—like right now?

That's why our Brain Highways participants first engage in playful approaches that we created for the sole purpose of assuring their nervous system, "I can handle now what I could not back then." The intentional playfulness of these approaches is key because we're not going to move forward if our nervous system shuts down before we even get started.

Our participants engage in three different approaches, in which we have put our own spin on techniques already known to address charged memories and unproductive, automated subconscious programming. The combination of these three spin-off approaches makes it possible for our participants to identify which subconscious programs are sabotaging their lives, to put date stamps on their charged memories (so that their past is no longer triggering and escalating their reactions in the present), and to help their brain and nervous system adopt more positive ways of thinking and acting—all on their own.

It's not that I don't want to share those approaches in this book. But when we teach our participants how to do this, we rely on many videos, audios, and handouts, along with individualized feedback that goes far beyond the scope of a book. We also do not even introduce these approaches until almost the end of our program. That's because by then our participants have already finished a lot of their lower brain development and have experienced that they can return to connection mode (if triggered) on their own. Such experiences and confidence are especially important groundwork for putting date stamps on charged memories.

To note, there are many skilled professionals who can absolutely help people get their date stamps (though, heads-up, they are not going to refer to their work that way). Since there are a variety of approaches that focus on the nervous system and body—and both are key to getting closure on a lingering charged memory—it often comes down to finding a professional who does whichever approach resonates the most with whoever is seeking help, as well as finding someone who can help connect the past to understanding behavior in the present.

Having a professional's guidance can be especially helpful when addressing volatile memories, which is why we also encourage many of our own participants to seek additional help as part of their reparative process. However, because there are so many personal variables, I do not think it's helpful to recommend specific approaches or professionals as being more beneficial than others. Instead, I trust that people will use the information they've gleaned about the nervous system as a guide to help them know what might be best for them.

A LOWER BRAIN REMINDER

A prior Brain Highways participant once summed up her life before she started to finish her lower brain development as part of repairing her nervous system's flexibility: "The best hope I had was to sort of figure out how to cope better, which took an exhausting amount of energy and left no time to actually enjoy life. And that was a seriously depressing message."

Part 2 presents what you need to know about a possible lower brain connection, including that completing this development is huge when it comes to restoring our nervous system's flexibility. So there's no need to say any more in this chapter other than to remind you of these important points: First, a lower brain connection is often the missing piece of the puzzle for those who have continued to struggle, especially after doing so many different approaches. But, second, if we want an easier life, finishing our lower brain development is not the *only* change we make. Some people become so excited about this component that they forget about all the other ways to restore their nervous system's flexibility. While finishing the lower brain development may be key for many people, we will always need to address all three parts of the nervous system's trifecta.

MORE ON THOSE SUBCONSCIOUS PROGRAMS

We first need to identify which of our subconscious programs are not helpful. For example, we may have only recently realized that saying something such as "I don't do emotions" is just a program that we downloaded from someone else or adopted all on our own.

But as a heads-up, most hardwired subconscious programs are not that easy to delete. Once a program is up and running, the subconscious mind then seeks confirming experiences to support the thought behind the program. For starters, if I begin to think, "Okay, I can feel emotions," my brain will quickly shut down that thought as I time travel to all those times that I never shed a tear, or became angry, or showed any other emotion. (See? I do *not* do emotions.)

That is why we do crossovers, tapping, or havening (all presented in Chapter 11) as part of the process for deleting and upgrading a subconscious program. We also start with a string of noncommittal sentences, in which our initial thoughts toward a new subconscious program change in only slight increments. For example, we might begin with "I'm curious how my life might be if I felt emotions." From there, we might say, "I am open to pondering whether it is safe for me to feel emotions." That may lead to "I am ready to start feeling emotions." Again, we are thinking those different thoughts while simultaneously doing movements that make it easier for all parts of our brain to consider them. We want our brain to contemplate the new thought without alerting the nervous system to sound the stress alarm. This incremental process is part of what eventually leads us to the new, upgraded program: "I feel emotions."

And yet actual life experiences—especially those that shatter what we thought was true—are always going to be the most powerful way to change a subconscious program. In such cases, our "brain hecklers" cannot say, "See? Told you so!" because this time, we had a very different experience.

MESSING WITH PRIOR EXPERIENCES

Sometimes, we can even unknowingly repair the nervous system.

My first teaching job was in the inner city at an elementary school with barbed wire fencing around its perimeter (which turned out to be a feeble attempt to deter the ongoing weekend vandalism). Veteran teachers at the school warned me to expect no parent support (there had never been a parent-teacher association) and that students had little or no interest in learning.

These teachers also volunteered that aggressive fist fights were commonplace during recess and that some of the kids were even known to set trash cans on fire—just for fun. Oh, and by the way, the most notorious of those students were the ones assigned to my fifth-grade classroom.

It is the first day of school, and my students are filtering into the room. They seem quite surprised as they view the wall completely covered with photos of Hawaii and sunsets. A colorful beach chair faces that wall, while a suitcase sits next to a small table that has dried fruit on a plate. The rest of the classroom walls are sectioned off with 30 equally sized, empty squares.

Once everyone is seated, I explain to my students, "Since this is your classroom, one of these squares is yours. It will be your personal space, where you can put up whatever you think is important to you."

I then point to the Hawaii wall. "Oh, and yes, throughout the year, you will be going on vacation, where you will fly to Hawaii, Room 21–style." I pick one of the students to help me show everyone what that means.

I open the suitcase and pull out a Hawaiian shirt, lei, and sunglasses. As I put these on the student, I say, "First, we'll make sure that you're dressed to go." I next pull magazines, headphones, and a Sony Walkman out of the suitcase. As intended, the Sony Walkman really catches their attention. Walkmans are the very cool portable cassette player that most people still do not own.

I hand the magazines, Walkman, and headphones to the student as I now explain how the class does the send-off. "Now we all wave as we say a lively, 'A-l-o-h-a!'" The vacationing student next models sitting on the beach chair, listening to the music, munching on the dried fruit, looking through the magazines, and gazing at the sunset—all as part of his vacation.

I now tell my students to look inside their desks and pull out the white envelope. When they open their envelope, they see $200 of Room 21 money. I share that at the end of each week, I will auction items that can only be bought with Room 21 currency. I explain that there are multiple ways to earn this money. However, this classroom money is also used to settle out-of-court payments, as well as in-court restitutions, which I say I will explain in a bit.

First, I continue by saying, "Classroom rules? There are none. Yet every student in this room is protected by four rights. You have the right to like yourself, which covers anyone saying anything belittling, mocking, cruel, or judgmental. You have the right to be safe, which covers anything that is a verbal threat or causes physical harm. You have the right to learn, which covers any disruptions and distractions that could interfere with your learning. You have the right to have your property protected, which covers stealing, as well as actions such as someone grabbing your hat right off your head. If someone violates any of your rights, you first try to settle out of court. If you violated someone else's right, then you pay the out-of-court settlement. But if you do not think you did so, then the case comes to our Room 21 Court of Civil Law."

The students are most definitely intrigued. None of this matches with their prior subconscious programs about school.

Each week, we also held a Court of Commendation. At that time, any student could stand and commend another student for doing something that stood out as positive during the week. The (student) judge would then instruct the (student) bailiff to give the commended person $20 (again, Room 21 money).

While inside our classroom everything was harmonious, this was still the same school in the same inner city. For example, it wasn't as though the weekend vandalism sprees ended; however, interestingly, Room 21 was never touched. And not surprisingly, almost all infractions of the students' rights happened during recess. However, while I saw many kids paying settlements to one another as soon as recess ended, I never saw anyone approach Darius. And yet Darius was probably known to be the biggest, toughest bully at the school.

The kids were most definitely afraid of Darius. At the same time, Darius had a swagger and confidence that impressed them. While Darius was now a model student inside the classroom, I had no illusions that he had suddenly turned into a Boy Scout during recess. No one was even approaching Darius for an out-of-court settlement—that is, until Tuan.

Tuan was a small, extraordinarily thin Vietnamese refugee. Yet it turns out that Tuan told Darius he had violated his right to be safe. We only knew that because during the Court of Commendation,

Darius stood up and said, "I'd like to commend Tuan. He's the only one who's had the guts to stand up to me for violating his right to be safe."

I do not think I can overstate what that experience must have been like for Darius, Tuan, and every student in that class. Almost four decades later, I can still remember that moment as though it just happened.

Not only did Darius never retaliate against Tuan for initiating an out-of-court settlement, but the toughest kid at the school commended Tuan—in front of everyone—for his courage. Within a few seconds, toughness was redefined for every kid in that room.

Back then, I did not know how moments like that, along with all the other ways Room 21 differed from traditional classrooms, were *disconfirming experiences*. Yet it turns out that disconfirming experiences can be reparative to our nervous system, and now I understand why.

Disconfirming experiences rattle our nervous system (in a good way) because they undeniably counter what our subconscious programs are expecting as *confirmation*. In the case of my students, they were already programmed to expect school to be boring and meaningless, or that they were too stupid to learn, or that they were going to be threatened at school, and more. But now my fifth graders were having lots of disconfirming experiences about school that most certainly messed with *and changed* their prior programs.

I share these examples because anyone can create disconfirming experiences in any environment, whether it is in the classroom, at home, at work, or at soccer practice—anywhere. I'm hoping you will be inspired to see what you might now come up with to help others delete one or more of their unproductive subconscious programs.

And how does doing that help you repair your own nervous system? Well, mirror neurons and the reliable reciprocity feature of our nervous system—where we feel good when we help someone else—are always at play. And so being the catalyst for others to change their programs is going to have a positive effect on your own nervous system's landscape as well.

NEW ROLES

Over the years, we have sometimes assigned the kids in our program to be our Brain Highways executives, becoming the leaders of a community project to make a significant difference in other people's lives. It has never mattered that many of these kids had diagnoses such as autism, ADHD, OCD, oppositional defiant disorder, and learning disabilities, or that some were nonverbal or known for their meltdowns. They were our executives.

Time and time again, the different groups of Brain Highways executives exceeded what anyone thought they might accomplish. Perhaps one community project stands out the most because something wildly unexpected happened. This was our Kids Why Not Campaign, during which 60 of our Brain Highways executives set out to widen people's views on mental health. The thought was "Who better than kids who had already struggled with their own mental health to teach others about this important topic?"

In addition to the educational part of this project, these executives also applied their creative talents to raise $4,000. That money was then used to purchase the same kind of cool brain apparatus and calming proprioceptive toys that the kids enjoyed at the Brain Highways Center. The executives presented all those purchases to the CAPS (Child and Adolescent Psychiatry Services) program at Rady Children's Hospital, specifically for the ward where children are kept if they've been assessed as being a danger to themselves or others. Before Brain Highways, a few of our executives themselves had already spent time in such wards.

As the campaign was coming to an end, the kids decided to

gather in small groups to write a "Dear Teacher" letter. The idea was to share what they thought teachers might want to understand about kids like them. The final letter reflected the recurring themes from each of their smaller group letters.

And then someone said, "Hey, why don't we turn this letter into a Dear Teacher video?" It seemed like a good idea, so we picked some of the executives to each say one line from their final letter. We intentionally shot the video in black and white and with no background music. It was just the kids, speaking from their experience and heart. The entire video was a little less than two minutes long.

Well, almost overnight the video went viral. At lightning speed, people in countries from all over the world kept viewing and sharing it. And just when we would think the video had run its course, another large worldwide social media platform would post it on their site, where it would rack up yet another 5 or 10 million views. To date, the kids' Dear Teacher video has more than 65 million views, along with hundreds of thousands of comments.

When reading those comments, it never mattered whether the person was a teacher, principal, school board member, parent, grandparent, or therapist—male or female, young or old. The gist of their comments was always the same in that people would say how the video made them tear up, cry, even sob, or how it pulled at their heart, broke their heart, opened their heart, melted their heart, or spoke to their heart.

There was one undeniable theme. While the kids were from San Diego, California, people from every continent were now "seeing" their own son or daughter or sister or brother or student or friend or relative—and many times, themselves—in that footage. Again and again, people thanked the kids for voicing what they themselves had always wanted to say but never thought they could.

So a less-than-two-minute video managed to break through the stigma that often prevents us from talking about mental health. Somehow, a group of kids—who likely would have never been considered to lead a project—made it safe for hundreds of thousands of people to be raw and open as they now shared their own thoughts and school experiences by way of a Facebook comment.

I also share this story because it underscores an important component when it comes to repairing our nervous system. Whoever we are and wherever we live, we all just want to be seen, understood, and appreciated *as is*. There's nothing more powerful than those kinds of reparative experiences.

For example, my older sister recently received an email from a student she taught back in 1997. This young woman wanted to tell her that she was now pursuing a teaching credential all because of her third-grade experience. She wrote that before third grade, she had always been shy and insecure. Yet my sister chose her to be the editor of a book that the class was writing about their city. This young woman wrote that, at the time, she was completely shocked to be chosen for this important role. But for the first time ever, *she felt seen and significant.* She went on to recall all the wonderful experiences she had in that editor role, including a chance to meet the city's mayor. The last line in her heartfelt email was "Thank you for seeing me."

We may never even know when we have created a life-changing, reparative experience for someone else—just by giving them a chance to shine.

THE LAST PART OF THE TRIFECTA

In Chapter 11, you learn how to resolve perceived threats so that you can quickly return to connection mode in real time. In this chapter, you have an opportunity to ponder where you might clear (repair) your nervous system's landscape so that those same stressors do not continually show up in your life.

So what is left to learn? We also need to know how to replenish our nervous system, which is the focus of the next and last chapter of this book.

13

~~~~~

REPLENISHING OUR
NERVOUS SYSTEM

You don't hear people say, "Oh, I don't have time to recharge my phone." Or "I'm ridiculously swamped, so maybe I'll recharge my phone in, like, two weeks from this Saturday." No one makes those kinds of comments because we already know that our phones can only go so long without being charged. We have also likely experienced our phone going completely dark after we kept ignoring signs that its battery was running low. And yet many people do not think that same recharging-our-cell-phone mindset applies to regularly recharging and replenishing our nervous system—but it does. While our nervous system may not be as quick as a phone to tell us when our battery is running low, it cannot be ignored for long.

HOW TIME GETS IN THE WAY

Suppose someone magically gives me six extra hours a day. Sounds great, right? But that will make no difference if I'm still holding on to certain thoughts.

For example, if I think that I'm only productive while I am at work or cleaning the house or figuring out how to get ahead in this world, then I will just use those extra hours to try to be more productive. If I worry about how others view me, I will use those extra hours to get people's approval. If I have framed myself as the only one who can ensure that everything gets done (whether this is at work or at home), I certainly cannot be off duty at any time. In all cases, it will not matter if I have even 10 extra hours a day. I am still never going to "find the time" to replenish.

Our general perception of time may also get in our way of replenishing our nervous system. For example, we often say, "I never have enough time," or "You wasted my time," as though time was a scarce commodity. But we do not ever think, "Wow! I get 24 hours a day—and that happens every day! A-m-a-z-i-n-g!"

Replenishing our nervous system has nothing to do with finding more time in our already overscheduled, hectic lives. Rather, it is about changing some perceptions about ourselves, reframing how we generally view time, and truly understanding why daily replenishing is key for a nervous system to work as intended.

WAYS TO REPLENISH

While there is no right way to replenish the nervous system, there are a few guidelines. First, there are those quiet activities that we do by ourselves, such as when we meditate, or garden, or fish, or go for a run. There are also those quiet activities that we do with others, such as when we take a yoga, tai chi, or qigong class. But here's the general idea behind this kind of replenishing: We pull ourselves away from the loud daily grind to somehow quiet our mind, and we feel better after we're done with whatever we chose to do.

A replenishing activity can also be anything that brings us a natural feeling of joy, to the degree that others can sense our passion. For example, from the time my oldest daughter took her first dance class at age four to today (she's now a young woman), she absolutely radiates whenever she is dancing. Those who watch her dance also feel the pure bliss that she is clearly experiencing (which I now realize can be explained by mirror neurons). She will always dance. It will always replenish her.

We also replenish our nervous system anytime we're in a flowing, creative state of mind. That's when we have only the vaguest idea of what we might create when we set out to write, or paint, or sculpt, or play music, or engage in any other kind of activity that inspires us. We also remain open to the possibility that we might even go in a completely different direction than what we thought when we first began. No problem—there is no "right way" to do something in a flow state.

Of course, we are always replenishing our nervous system whenever we practice calming actions while in connection mode. Here, we get a two-for-one. We replenish our nervous system, but such practice also helps us automate such responses—which is key to replacing our prior automated stress reactions.

If replenishing your nervous system every day is something new to you, I highly recommend that you create a menu of at least six ways that you like to replenish. Then, first thing in the morning, decide what you are going to do that day and when. View that time as having the same kind of priority and importance as though you had scheduled a work meeting or appointment for that same time. In other words, even if your day gets really busy, your replenishing time is not negotiable.

While spending any amount of time to replenish is better than spending no time at all, we generally need at least a 20-minute block of time to make a difference to our nervous system. Again, returning to the cell phone example, recharging for just a few minutes is not going to have much of an effect.

Long ago, I started taking 20 minutes a day to replenish. But over time, I discovered that if I wanted to stay grounded—especially if chaos was surrounding me—I needed more than just one 20-minute block of time. It turns out that I need a minimum of three 20-minute blocks spread throughout the day to replenish. If for some reason I have enough time to do only one or two blocks, my nervous system lets me know. I can now really feel the difference on those days, as compared to when I do all three blocks of time.

Many Brain Highways parents initially tell me, "You just don't get it. There is nowhere in my house that's quiet, and there is no chance that my family will ever leave me alone for even five minutes." But again, it all comes back to what we believe. When I started meditating more than 33 years ago, my girls were three and four years old. I would go into my bedroom to meditate right before dinner. My kids and husband knew that they were only allowed to enter my room if the house was on fire. Pretty much anything short of that, they were on their own.

Rather quickly, my husband and kids not only followed the rules but also started encouraging me to go meditate. It did not take a rocket scientist to figure out why. Plain and simple—a much nicer, more grounded, and calmer mom and wife emerged from that room after meditating for 20 minutes. And that's the point that many people do not often initially get about replenishing. We replenish just as much for others as we do for ourselves.

Decades later, I now sometimes meditate in my home office and at random times. On occasion, my husband will open the door to ask me something, thinking I'm working and not meditating. But as soon as he sees me meditating, he quickly shuts the door as I hear him mutter a sincere "Oh, so sorry." I am thinking that is what 33-plus years of family replenishing training looks like.

Of course, kids also have a nervous system that needs to be replenished. If possible, we encourage our family program participants to set aside a time each day where everyone is replenishing at the same time. That does not mean that everyone is replenishing in the same way. For example, kids may use this time to create with Legos, to draw, or do anything else they like that fits the general criteria for replenishing.

REPLENISHING WITH OTHERS

While the nervous system is all about being safe, it is equally about being connected to others. As humans, we are wired to be with people.

While we replenish our nervous system by doing daily quiet and creative activities, we also replenish it by becoming part of a community. Our community is one that reflects our interests and values, where we spend time with members in the group that we especially like—and where we feel uplifted after we've been with those people.

In a similar way, we replenish our nervous system when we volunteer. While there are set volunteer positions, there is nothing to stop us from creating our own volunteer job. This is when we offer one of our talents to help others.

For example, maybe we love photography. If so, when we go to the beach or elsewhere to shoot photos, that would fall under the quiet and creative kind of replenishing. But if we now also volunteer to be the photographer at library events, or to do portraits of military families, or to take photos of animals at a shelter (to help them find a home), we are replenishing while being with others. Mirror neurons and the reciprocity nature of our nervous system will guarantee that we feel replenished whenever we help others.

SLEEP

In recent times, the need to get enough sleep has made it to prime time. Such informational campaigns also underscore justifiable concerns about the blue light coming from our electronic devices—how that can mess with our natural circadian rhythms, which then interferes with our ability to fall asleep. All true.

It goes without saying that sleep is certainly an important part of replenishing our nervous system. However, when viewing sleep from the lens of the nervous system, there are some important considerations that I do not usually see included with typical discussions on sleep. For example, we are now told that we need somewhere between seven and nine hours of sleep every night.

Yet, to me, the first criterion when assessing our sleep would be to ask ourselves these questions: How do I feel after I wake up each morning? Refreshed? Ready to greet the new day? Or tired, dragging, as I make myself get out of bed? That's because if our nervous system is depleted and we are running on empty, it will not matter if we sleep 12 hours. We will still wake up feeling exhausted.

On the other hand, if we're concurrently resolving, repairing, and replenishing our nervous system, not only do we wake up ready to jump out of bed, but we also likely require less sleep than before. For example, I used to need a minimum of eight hours of sleep each night, though nine hours was even better—and I'm talking about when I was much younger. But once I started resolving threats in real time, repairing parts of my nervous system, and doing a minimum of three replenishing activities throughout the day, that all changed. Today I couldn't sleep more than seven hours a night if you paid me, and I feel equally refreshed and great after getting just six hours of sleep. (Keep in mind that I've never had a cup of coffee in my entire life. So when I say I wake up "ready to go," it's without caffeine.)

There are also all the people who have trouble falling asleep, or who keep waking up throughout the night, or who have frequent nightmares. However, when faced with common sleep problems, we do not often connect what is going on *during the day* to what is showing up as a sleep problem at night.

For starters, high levels of cortisol—which is a given if we're stuck in protection mode—can greatly interfere with our sleep. But our brain is also sorting out our day while we sleep. What remains unresolved during the day may now show up as problematic sleep, causing us to wake up many times throughout the night or even have a nightmare.

It's not surprising that once Brain Highways participants start resolving threats in real time, repairing their nervous system (which includes completing their lower brain development), and engaging in daily replenishing activities, they notice how their sleep is improving. Of course, as always, I never claim that *everything* is related to our lower brain and nervous system. There are certainly other reasons why people may struggle with their sleep. But there is also the possibility that how we sleep at night is linked to the current state of our nervous system.

GOING BRAVE

When we go brave as part of *repairing* our nervous system, we follow a specific process to override a distorted fear. When we go brave as part of *replenishing* our nervous system, we give our nervous system various opportunities to differentiate situations in which we feel uncomfortable from those that cause us to feel true fear. With the former, we are wiring our brain *to be okay with uncertainty*, since the unknown is what often triggers our stress. The more times we go brave whenever we are uncertain of the outcome, the more our nervous system becomes comfortable—and even confident—about such situations in the future.

Of course, how we go brave will look different among people simply because we do not all view each situation in the same way. For example, suppose Keisha feels uncomfortable about voicing her opinions. When she decides to speak up at the work meeting, she is going brave. And yet when Amara decides to share her thoughts at that same meeting, her nervous system yawns. That's because Amara is comfortable with sharing her opinions.

Whenever we go brave to replenish our nervous system, there are always two general guidelines. We intentionally choose to do something for which the outcome is uncertain (Keisha did not know how her opinion would be received), and we feel uncomfortable about whatever we have decided to do (Keisha was uneasy about speaking up). While there is no rule on how often we go brave, it's always good to keep reminding our nervous system that we can deal with uncertainty and feeling uncomfortable.

ANYTHING MIGHT HAPPEN WHEN WE GO BRAVE (AND THAT'S THE POINT)

Speaking in front of a large audience is not going brave for me. For decades I've spoken to hundreds of educators at large school districts and national educational conferences. So when I accepted an invitation to be one of the speakers at a TEDx event, I wasn't really concerned about speaking to 200 people in a live audience while the event was being streamed to another 8,000 people.

However, I hadn't done a presentation outside the Brain Highways Center for more than 10 years. That meant I had become quite comfortable with having total control of the format, room setup, and more. Since I was feeling a bit uncomfortable about relinquishing that control and speaking in an unfamiliar auditorium at the University of California, I initially thought the TEDx invitation could be a mild going-brave opportunity for me. Once I was informed that all speakers were required to attend a technical run-through practice, I felt better. But that's when I learned about the other nonnegotiable rules.

First, we were shown a countdown clock on the wall as we were told that no presentation could last longer than 13 minutes. There was more. As soon as any speaker went past that time, the stage manager would immediately appear at the side of the stage. If the speaker was still talking after 30 seconds, the stage manager would then escort that person off the stage. (And they weren't bluffing. That is exactly what happened to one of the speakers!) So, yes, the countdown clock and strict 13-minute time limit most certainly added some unexpected pressure.

We were then told that we had to stay within a small radius on the stage while doing our presentation. Since I like to move around a lot, that rule also created some stress. In addition, I was informed that TEDx speakers were not allowed to hold a clipboard. While I acknowledge that having an outline on a clipboard to occasionally glance at (to keep me on track) is outdated and not high-tech, that was what I had been doing when speaking to groups at the Brain Highways Center. The organizers said that I could instead give them my outline as slides, which could then appear on the teleprompter-like screen just below the stage. That way I could click through the slides to stay on track, but I would be the only person who could see what was on the screen. My going-brave ranking for this event was definitely increasing.

By the time the TEDx event came around, I had done a variety of calming approaches to put me at ease about relinquishing all control and following their rules. I was excited and ready to share what I am so passionate about wanting others to know.

As promised, the clock on the wall starts the countdown as soon as

I step onto the stage. I go straight to my center-of-the-stage spot and begin to talk. At the same time, I also subtly click the clicker in the palm of my hand to start the slides with my outline.

Only nothing happens. The screen is completely blank! I don't stop talking (after all, the clock is ticking away), but I'm also thinking, *"I don't believe this!"* So I keep talking, as I click again and again and again. But all I see is a blank screen.

I am now about two minutes into my presentation. I know that I'm somehow still talking, but it's like I am in a parallel universe, because another part of my brain is still simultaneously assessing this disaster.

And then I have this horrible thought. What if whoever is overseeing my outline slides doesn't understand that they are only for me? What if I every time I have clicked, my outline slides have been appearing on the wall behind me for the entire audience to see? But how I am supposed to suddenly turn around to check?

Miraculously, I am still talking away. At about three minutes in, I resign myself to the reality of my situation. In that parallel universe inside my brain, I decide that I need to accept that I'm doing this presentation without any outline and hope that I still finish on time.

Then, only 30 seconds after making that decision, I see that my first slide has suddenly appeared on the screen! But I am long past that part in my talk. Once again, I keep talking, but I'm now clicking away while surreptitiously glancing at the screen to see if I can get to the slide that matches where I'm at. At about four minutes in, victory! Everything is lined up and finally working as intended.

As another grace, I finish my presentation before the countdown clock runs out of time. Amazingly, the audience's vigorous, long applause suggests that I may have somehow pulled off the impossible.

THE EXTRA INCENTIVE FOR GOING BRAVE

Sometimes when we go brave, everything goes *better* than we imagined. Yet there are also those times—like my TEDx event—when we cannot even imagine the worst-case scenario that becomes our reality. However, in both scenarios, the primary point of going brave never changes. Each going brave experience wires us to have the confidence that *we can survive feeling uncomfortable.*

For example, my response to my TEDx debacle was not "Well, I'm not doing any more presentations unless they are at my Brain Highways Center." To the contrary, after the TEDx talk, I agreed to be the only speaker at a full-day event sponsored by the American Academy of Pediatrics, which also pushed me out of my comfort zone.

This largely attended event was held at what turned out to be a very crowded banquet room at a resort, where the organizers ended up shoving the maximum number of tables as closely together as possible. That still left an overflow of people who were not placed at any table. While this event did not even come close to the challenges of the TEDx talk, once again, I had to think quickly on my feet, since I had planned on having the group do many movements that help the brain. You might even say that I accepted this speaking engagement *because* of my TEDx experience. After all, I survived that ordeal, right? (And what could be worse?)

Most importantly, continuously going brave for short-term challenges now paves the way for our brain and nervous system to feel confident about taking on bigger risks. For example, maybe we now leave our predictable job for one that excites us, or we move to a state we've always wanted to live in, or we try something that we previously didn't feel like we could ever do. That's because while uncertainty is always inherent to risk-taking, it is no longer a deterrent for us. After all, our going-brave experiences have taught our nervous system that it can be okay with (and survive) the unknown. We are now confident to have experiences that we previously would not have even considered.

DAILY GRATITUDE AND SURPRISES

Amazingly, scientists can now pinpoint where gratitude shows up in the brain. We have also learned that when we express and receive gratitude, our brain releases two feel-good neurotransmitters: dopamine and serotonin.

I have come to think of gratitude in two ways. The first kind of gratitude is what I call our once-a-year Thanksgiving appreciations. Here, family members and friends will often take turns expressing what they're generally grateful for, such as having a home, clean water, and a loving family. There is nothing wrong with any of that. But that once-a-year kind of gratitude is not likely going to change our brain and nervous system in any significant way.

With that in mind, about 12 years ago, I decided to challenge myself to note what I was grateful for *only on that specific day* before I went to sleep each night. In truth, I did not believe this challenge would be hard, since I think of myself as a person who usually sees the world in a positive light. And yet there I was on that first night, struggling to come up with even one single thing I was grateful for *on that day*. I was shocked when I came up with nothing.

So when I spotted a yellow swallowtail the next morning, I was like, "Yes! Tonight, I'm going to be able to say that I was grateful to have seen a beautiful butterfly." However, my nighttime gratitude list quickly became longer and longer. That is when I had this realization: My challenge was actually priming me to be more mindful about what had always been in my day. Only now was I noticing all those small, wondrous happenings.

While we present this same gratitude challenge to our Brain Highways participants, we also have our parents and kids do something we call "Gratitude Surprises." For this activity, both the parents and the kids think of something they're grateful for about each other. But they do not share aloud what they are thinking. Instead, they write their gratitude on a slip of paper. Then they hide that note somewhere that they know the intended family member will come across it sooner rather than later.

For example, a parent may hide a gratitude note inside her child's backpack that says, "I am grateful that you get ready for school all on your own." Or a child may secretly place a sticky note on the bathroom mirror (where his dad stands when shaving) that says, "I am grateful that you leave work early to come to my baseball games."

The Brain Highways kids often say that they have more fun creating gratitude surprise notes than receiving them (though they enjoy those as well), whereas their parents either beam or tear up (or do both) whenever they share whatever gratitude surprise they have received from their kids.

> We are in class, and a mom of a teen raises her hand to share her surprise gratitude experience.
>
> "Since I'm about to do the laundry, just like I always do, I go over to the laundry basket. When I lift the lid, I see a gratitude note from my son."
>
> She is tearing up now. She pauses and then smiles in a way that we imagine she probably did when she first came across the surprise. "The note said, 'Mom, I am so grateful that you always make sure that I have clean clothes.'"

It does not ultimately matter how we weave gratitude into our daily life. But its undeniable positive effect is why we want gratitude to be part of replenishing our nervous system.

PLAY

When it comes to babies, most people do not hesitate to be playful. For example, parents all over the world play peek-a-boo with their little ones. And when we watch parents play this simple game, we notice that they seem to enjoy it as much as their babies—especially when their baby squeals with delight or lights up when they open their hands to reveal their face. Parents will also make their baby's mealtime playful, such as pretending the food in the spoon is a plane flying into the hangar (which just so happens to be the baby's opened mouth). Yet it isn't long before such natural playfulness quickly disappears.

Whether we realize it or not, much of the world has been busy imprinting the opposite message about being playful, with some people even associating being playful as something frivolous. However, in terms of the nervous system, we need to play as much as we need food and water. That's why being playful—doing something for pure fun that has no "right" way to act—is yet another way to replenish our nervous system. For starters, it is impossible to be playful and be in protection mode at the same time. But true play can also release endorphins (the body's feel-good chemicals), boost creativity, and present opportunities to engage with others when everyone is in connection mode.

To give our families a chance to play together in ways they have not likely experienced, we present them with a list of out-of-the-ordinary ideas. Examples of favorite activities include dressing a chair, painting with ice cubes, becoming dog trainers (where the kids are the trainers and their parents are the dogs), and having a backward dinner (where everyone calls one another by how their name would be if spelled backward, wears their clothing backward, and starts the meal with dessert). Laughter, humor, and joy are always going to replenish the nervous system.

But there are other simple ways to infuse playfulness into our lives. For example, "Fifi from France" became legendary among my girls' childhood friends after I one day whimsically pretended to be Fifi. In a French accent guaranteed to make anyone from France cringe, it was Fifi, the waitress from France—not my girls' mom—who was serving everyone their lunch. Of course, since Fifi did not know anyone's names, she addressed everyone by saying, "Mon Chéri," which only made the kids giggle even more.

Now, while I knew that my kids and their friends enjoyed that playful lunch, I did not anticipate what followed. For the longest time, whenever this same group of kids came to our house, they would always ask, "Will Fifi be showing up today?"

There is no limit on ways that we might be playful. Here's an example of what I mean: When my grandson was born, my daughter received a gift for her son from a nine-year-old. She had made her son a doll, and the gesture was lovely. But there was one problem. The doll's face looked—it's hard to describe this any other way—scary. At first, I thought my daughter and her husband were exaggerating when they only half-jokingly said that this doll could haunt a child for life. But when I saw it, I have to admit, I also thought it might be a good idea to keep this doll away from a child.

And there was yet another problem. My daughter and her husband also recognized that this sweet girl clearly did not see her handmade doll this way. She had obviously put lots of time and love into making this gift. So they didn't feel right about just tossing the doll into the trash.

And that's how this doll became the source of much playfulness in their house. It started when my son-in-law hid the doll inside the kitchen cupboard, knowing that my daughter would see it when she went to grab her morning teacup. When my daughter opened the cabinet door and unexpectedly saw the doll now perched on the shelf—staring right at her—she, of course, laughed.

Then, without her husband knowing it, my daughter hid the doll where she knew he would come across it. He, too, burst out laughing when the doll caught him by surprise. Before long, the hiding and unexpected reappearance of this "scary" doll became a joyful, playful game in their house.

WHERE WE GO FROM HERE

By now I hope you are convinced of this truth: We are biologically wired to have an easier life. That basic statement holds true for everyone. There are no asterisks by certain people's names as being an exception. We all come into this world with a nervous system that innately wires us for survival, but one that also equally wires us for connection.

The challenge is not to aimlessly search for a new nervous system. Rather, it is to restore the one we already have if, for whatever reason, it has lost its flexibility. It is that flexibility that gives us more access to the part of our nervous system that's wired for connection, the part that allows us to show up as the best version of ourselves.

Throughout this book, I present many analogies to help you understand key concepts. It seems only fitting that I conclude with one last analogy to sum up those main points. It might also give you something to visualize as you move forward.

For this analogy, suppose the big ocean represents *life* and each of us is given a boat to navigate the high seas. Well, since it is the ocean, it's no surprise that we sometimes encounter rough waters, or huge swells, or maybe even a tsunami. When that happens, there we go! We are quickly tossed overboard—right smack into the ocean—where we now find ourselves treading water. However, that's not a problem if we know how to get back to the boat.

But what if we've forgotten how to do that? Then we will need to keep treading water, all the time, which is exhausting. After a while, we won't remember that we even had a boat or that we ever experienced smooth sailing. We are so preoccupied with trying to keep our head above water.

Of course, we're not alone in the water. We're surrounded by all the other people who are also endlessly treading water and trying to stay afloat.

But we're supposed to get back to the boat. So how do we do

that? Well, fortunately, we also come equipped with our very own innate life preserver (a.k.a. a flexible nervous system). That is what gets us back to the boat. That is what sometimes even prevents us from falling overboard in the first place, allowing us to stay the course as we pass through rough waters. That is what ensures that we spend much more time smooth sailing than treading water.

What happens, then, when we're tossed overboard without ever completing our lower brain development? Well, we will still be treading water—but now with 10-pound weights tied to our wrists and ankles! And what if we are stuck in protection mode, which is even more likely if we haven't completed our lower brain development? Again, we will still be treading water—but now while wearing a full suit of armor!

If that was not challenging enough, it gets worse. While we're totally preoccupied with trying to keep our head above water, others seem oblivious to our plight. They still expect us to pay attention, read, write, make friends, be better organized—the list goes on.

Worst of all, people now frame who they think we are based on how we act while treading water—*wearing armor!* They seem to have forgotten who we really are—the way we were back on the boat.

On the boat, it was easy to learn. We could naturally show compassion, curiosity, and creativity, and we had positive connections with others. But since we've been treading for such a long time, we, too, have forgotten about life on the boat. So now we also believe what others think and say about us. And unless something changes, this is how it is going to be. After all, we can't be in the water and in the boat at the same time.

We could keep this analogy going by pointing out the futility of trying to change, or control, or fix the ocean or to blame the waves for what happens to us. Yet we do have the power to make sure that we restore our life preserver (if needed) so we can always carry it with us wherever we go. Sure, it will always be that same unpredictable ocean. But that life preserver will return us to the boat whenever we go overboard. It will also make it possible to navigate those seas with a new sense of calm and joy.

Of course, no one knows for certain where our boat will go. That's our individual journey. But to arrive at wherever we are headed, we cannot keep treading endlessly in the water.

Luckily, that is not going to be you. Not only do you now know how to get back to the boat, but you also know that *you are innately wired to be there.* That combined knowledge makes you very powerful. It is what leads you to a life filled with more joy, peace, kindness, creativity, curiosity, and compassion—instead of a life saddled with endless stress and struggle.

But most of all, you now know this truth: An easier life is not a desert mirage or a fool's paradise. An easier life is even more than a mere possibility. If we choose to change our brain and restore our nervous system's flexibility—which all of us can do—then an easier life becomes *our reality.*

In that sense, perhaps a life of chaos and struggle was always the illusion. While such a life appears to be etched in stone, it is not. But we only *experience* that truth firsthand once we are back in the boat. And while each of us may sail somewhere different on our ocean's journey, we will all have this in common: We are now living the easier life.

ACKNOWLEDGMENTS

Without Brain Highways, there would never be this book. Over the last two decades, many people have played an integral part of the Brain Highways journey, and so I want to acknowledge some of those key players here.

I start with where it all began. I thank Sue Niebecker (who was the vice president of a Wells Fargo branch) for making it possible for Paul Ecke Central Elementary School to receive that first grant and Gregg Sonken, the principal of Paul Ecke Central, who okayed that first Brain Lab and supported every wild idea that I presented.

Thanks go to all the parents who volunteered at the various Brain Labs at different schools. With your help and commitment, so many more kids participated in the Brain Labs than I initially imagined. I thank Margie Thompson, who took the time to answer my endless questions about visual and auditory processing in those early days and who generously paid for all the equipment in that first Brain Lab.

Thanks go to all the principals who have supported Brain Highways. I especially thank Emily Andrade, Dr. Elizabeth O'Toole, and Dr. Ray O'Toole (yes, they are married, but they were principals at different schools), since they were pioneer principals in my mind. These three were among the first to embrace Brain Highways at their respective schools, including providing the funding and logistics to train their teachers. And of course, I thank all the teachers who have been more than willing to "see" their students through the lens of incomplete lower-brain development and being stuck in protection mode. I know that their students greatly appreciate their willingness to make changes so they can learn with ease and joy.

I thank each of the 20,000 (and counting) Brain Highways participants—all those preschoolers, elementary school kids, teens, adults (mostly parents), and even senior citizens who have enrolled in our Brain Highways programs. Extra thanks go to all the adults and kids (some of whom have now become adults) who first shared their stories with me so that I could then share them with others who are just starting this journey. While I suspect that they would not have minded if I had used their real names in the various stories that appear in this book, I changed them anyway to honor their privacy.

But there was one child I do need to acknowledge by name: Adrian Galvan. I have said again and again that Adrian was by far the best teacher I ever had on this journey and that he, more than anyone, shaped what this program has become. For years, we have shown our Brain Highways participants a video of Adrian that spans 11 years of his life, starting when he was a nonverbal six-year-old who was known for his hours-long tantrums and diagnosed with autism and mental retardation (those were the exact words of his diagnosis back then). That video ends in a way that no one could have imagined. To date, thousands of Brain Highways participants have been moved and inspired by his story as they "see" their own son and daughter at the beginning of his video and then watch who Adrian becomes—an articulate leader, someone who embraces learning (even researching how to make his own boat and then sailing it on the bay), and a Steven Spielberg rival for genius when it comes to the innovative films he creates.

To note, Adrian was the first child I had ever met with those challenges. And yet back then, for whatever reason, Adrian kindly allowed me to try one idea after another on him; in this way, he became my teacher, showing me which ideas were keepers and which were clearly not. More importantly, he showed me that the most caring, thoughtful, insightful soul on this earth had somehow just been trapped, as we all watched the true Adrian emerge. He is undoubtably one of the most authentic, empathetic, kindest human beings you will ever meet. I thank Adrian for being my most amazing teacher and for removing any doubt that we all have the power to change our brain. I also know that thousands of families would like to thank him for the hope he has given them by sharing his story.

Thanks go to all the Brain Highways staff, past and present. There would be no Brain Highways without them. Whether their role is (or was) behind the scenes or working alongside the participants, they always show how much they care about each of them.

I thank all the doctors, physical therapists, occupational therapists, and psychologists who have referred those they work with to Brain Highways and continue to do so, even though I have only ever met a handful of them. Our participants share that these professionals refer them after seeing transformative changes in their patients who have participated in Brain Highways. So I also thank these professionals for encouraging their patients to seek ways to empower themselves.

While I cannot even begin to count all the books on the brain and nervous system that I have devoured over the past two decades, the work of the following individuals has been the most influential on what has become the Brain Highways program. In the order that I found their work, I thank Svea Gold, Sally Goddard, Bruce Lipton, Jon Kabat-Zinn, Nick Ortner, Peter Levine, Bessel van der Kolk, and Steven Porges.

I am grateful to all who read the first draft of this book and offered their helpful feedback. A special thanks go to two good friends: Victor Cross, whose comments often pointed to where readers without prior knowledge of Brain Highways might feel as though they were left in the fog, and Tracy Moran, whose copyeditor eyes for typos, missing punctuation, syntax, and more graced the first draft so that others could read the book without those distractions. From there, thanks go to the impressive professionals at Greenleaf Book Group who collectively brought their expertise and skills to take that first manuscript and transform it into a final book.

And finally, I thank my wonderful family. Thanks to my one-of-a-kind parents, Marvin and Arline Sokol, who raised me to ask questions, encouraged me to "go brave" and be different, and showed me unconditional love and support for whatever I chose to do.

I thank my son-in-law Casey, who first ventured into the Brain Highways Center after his student claimed that her new core strength came from developing her lower brain. He then became so interested in what we were doing that he became part of our weekend staff, which led to him meeting my daughter (and the rest is history).

Thanks go to my son-in-law Marty for never squashing my enthusiasm whenever I share something new about the brain and nervous system. (I acknowledge that not every son-in-law has to be excited about neurobiology.)

I'm grateful to my niece, Colleen, for all her artistic contributions to the program; to my nephew Cameron for his time working at the Brain Highways Center (his first job); and to my nephew David, who lets me bounce ideas off him and then always gives me honest, insightful feedback.

I thank my young grandchildren, Logan, Sutton, and Zoe, for allowing me to try approaches on them (even if they have no awareness that I am doing so), since I never knew any of this information when their moms were young.

Thanks go to my sisters, Marcia and Joanne, for often being the first volunteers for any spin-off approach that I have created.

I thank my daughter Callan for being the one who initially called me out (a very long time ago) when I did not think Brain Highways needed to be on social media (and then helped me enter that world) and for more recently calling me out when I said that I could not see how I could turn a program with hundreds of videos, audios, and handouts, as well as individualized support, into a book—to which she bluntly said, "Just write the book, Mom. You'll figure it out."

I thank my daughter Kiley, whom we never imagined, when she was my eager Brain Highways helper at age 14, would one day end up being the skilled, dedicated, and compassionate director of all the Brain Highways programs.

And, of course, I especially thank my husband, Jim, first for his technical expertise, which made it possible to create materials that are now sent all around the world, and for being our first go-to guy whenever some part of our infrastructure crashes. I also thank Jim for his amazing creativity and artistry, which shows up in the countless program photos he has taken and videos he has filmed— all while still doing his day job. And last, I thank Jim for allowing me to include him in so many stories in this book, for being an incredible partner and friend that I've known for nearly 50 years, and for waiting ever so patiently for the "right" book to be dedicated to him.

Appendix A

~~~~~~

A QUICK GUIDE TO
CONNECTION MODE'S LINGO

CONNECTION MODE: When we are in connection mode, it is easy to be present, curious, creative, compassionate, considerate, playful, and interact with others in a most positive way.

RUNNING THE "GOLD": The gold here refers to the activation of the neural circuitry that runs from the heart to the brain whenever we are in connection mode.

PROTECTION MODE: When we are in protection mode (and operating from our primitive, survival part of our brain), we are reacting with a fight, flight, freeze, or dissociative response, which is intended to protect us from the imminent threat.

SURGING: When we surge, adrenaline and other hormones pump through our body to give us energy to either fight or flee the imminent threat.

DORSAL DIVING: We do a dorsal dive when our nervous system decides that fight and flight options are not viable, so immobilization or dissociation are now the best ways to protect us from the imminent threat.

NO-DATE-STAMP MEMORIES: Whenever the brain does not perceive that a threat was resolved, that charged memory becomes stuck in limbo, where the brain now believes and acts as though the prior threat is still happening in the present.

NEVER-FORGET-THIS TAGS: From the brain's view, any charged memory without resolution has now become an even bigger threat, as though such memories have been tagged with a flashing red light that reminds the brain to stay hypervigilant.

SCREEN 2: Screen 2 is where our subconscious life plays out, which includes not only helpful, automated actions that make our everyday life easy but also all the unproductive programs that we subconsciously downloaded as a child and all the charged, unresolved memories that are still waiting for closure.

BUILDING INTO THE STRUCTURE: We build into the structure when we make modifications to meet others where they are at, based on what we understand about their current brain profile and how the nervous system works. When we build into the structure, we also honor that we are not all wired the same and ensure that everyone stays in connection mode.

GOING BRAVE: We go brave by intentionally putting ourselves in situations that challenge us to take risks and go beyond our comfort zone. When we go brave, we teach our brain and nervous system that it is okay to feel uncertain and uncomfortable—and that we do not have to react to everything as though we are being attacked by a tiger.

OUR NERVOUS SYSTEM AT A GLANCE

The Gotcha

- The survival parts of our nervous system are laser-focused on protecting us from danger.

- However, our nervous system cannot distinguish imaginary threats from real ones.

- That "hiccup," along with our nervous system's zest for keeping us safe, means that its risk assessment is wrong most of the time.

Impersonal and Personal

- Our nervous system is impersonal since it is just doing its job when it puts us in protection mode.

- But our nervous system is also very personal in that it scans our entire history in a split second to decide whether something is a threat or not.

- If our nervous system deems something is a threat, it signals the brain and body to respond in physiological ways that are intended to help keep us safe from harm.

How Our Higher Centers of the Brain Get in the Way

- Since our conscious brain does not function at our nervous system's superpower speed, it is never consulted in any risk assessment.

- But since our conscious mind has been kept in the dark, it wants to know what has happened once it gets involved.

- Since the brain does not like uncertainty, it has no qualms about concocting a story to explain our behavior or to make sense of what has happened.

- If we believe the concocted story is true, we may now carry it with us long past the original event—and that story alone is what often keeps us in protection mode.

How We Respond

- Our nervous system (again, all by itself) decides what kind of protective reaction we will do in response to a threat.

- A fight (power over) response makes the predator fear us and retreat.

- A flight response gets us away from the predator.

- A freeze (immobilization) response makes us "invisible" so that the predator might not notice us.

- A dissociative response makes it possible to "check out" so that we do not feel whatever physical or emotional pain is too much for us to handle at that time.

- No matter the protective-mode response, we need to resolve the threat so that we can return to connection mode.

How Protection Mode Messes Us Up

- If we do not know how to resolve threats (real or perceived), we greatly increase the likelihood of becoming stuck in protection mode.

- When we spend so much of our life in protection mode, our physiology starts to change to adapt to our new hypervigilant view of the world.

- Unfortunately, such maladaptation only makes us even more reactive.

- When we are in protection mode, the higher centers of our brain also go offline, so logic, rational thinking, compassion, reflection, and learning are all MIA.

The Choice

- We cannot be in protection mode and connection mode at the same time. This is always an either-or binary system.

- Even if we are currently stuck in protection mode, it is possible for us to restore our nervous system's flexibility.

- That way, we can spend more time in connection mode, as well as easily bounce back if we have shifted into protection mode. (Recall that there is no scenario in which everyone stays in connection mode *all the time*.)

The Nervous System's Trifecta

- For our nervous system to work as intended, we adopt a trifecta approach that focuses on resolving, replenishing, and repairing—and we do not gloss over any of these parts.

- We need to know how to resolve threats *in real time* so that we can quickly return to connection mode.

- We need to repair our nervous system's landscape so that we can change whatever is continually keeping our nervous system in high alert.

- We need to replenish our nervous system daily so that it's continually nourished.

The Good News

- Whether we are young or old, rich or poor, a rock star or a mountain climber—our nervous system works the same way, no matter who we are.

- That means that all of us are wired for connection, as much as we are wired for survival.

- That also means that all of us can restore our nervous system's flexibility at any time in our life.

Appendix C

THE LOWER BRAIN CONNECTION

That First Year of Life

- The brain has a natural way of organizing itself—but we often get in its way of doing that.

- During the first year of life (or sometimes for even a little longer), babies are supposed to complete their lower brain development by doing specific movements to integrate primitive reflexes, creeping on their belly (the army commando movement), and then crawling on all fours.

- Engaging in those specific movements provides a solid foundation for the higher centers of the brain to build on.

- Developing the lower brain also gives the baby automatic brain functions that he or she will use for nearly everything in life.

- Without understanding why such movements are necessary, many parents may not realize that they did not provide opportunities for these early developmental stages to evolve naturally.

- In other cases, babies may have done these specific movements but not for a long enough time to have fully integrated their primitive reflexes and completed their lower brain development.

- It is also possible that some babies had undetected musculoskeletal restrictions or weaknesses that prevented them from doing these movements *as intended*—even when given the opportunity. (If new parents notice that their baby is creeping or crawling in a compensatory way, pediatric physical therapists are trained to assess and treat such problems.)

What Can Happen

- If we skip over any part of the lower brain development, a myriad of problems will often show up early on or later in life.

- Such struggles can include (but are not limited to) problems with sensory integration, focus, anxiety, spatial awareness, speech, auditory processing, visual processing, coordination, transitions, reading, writing, relationships, and learning with ease and joy.

- Incomplete lower brain development also skews our neuroception and interoception, making it challenging for us to interpret safety and danger cues accurately and to even sense our own body needs. In such cases, we may have little or no awareness that we are hungry or full, invading someone's space, or playing too roughly.

- Poor and distorted neuroception and interoception will then cause misunderstandings and the likelihood that we frequently experience a disconnect with others.

A Possible Missing Piece of the Puzzle

- Not addressing the lower brain connection may explain why prior approaches to help our nervous system did not move us forward or did not yield as much change as we had hoped.

- Integrating retained primitive reflexes and completing the lower brain development are key when it comes to restoring the nervous system's overall flexibility and resilience.

- If, when repairing our nervous system, we gloss over any of this underdevelopment (as in we do not integrate primitive reflexes and complete our lower brain development), then we will feel as though we are always resolving threats and never truly feel replenished.

- At any age, any of us can integrate retained primitive reflexes and finish our lower brain development.

- Once we have done so, we will have finally acquired those automatic, basic brain functions.

- With such circuitry now in place, many misunderstandings and stressors will no longer be present in our life.

- That then makes it easier for us to get out of protection mode and restore our nervous system's flexibility.

Appendix D

THE NINE TAPPING POINTS

Flexible Guidelines

- While people often tap in the order presented later in this appendix, it does not matter if you start somewhere else or if you skip a point (or two) when going through a tapping round.

- There are also no set rules for how many times you tap on each point.

- A loose guideline might be to tap at least 10 to 20 times on every point before moving on to the next one and to tap at least three full rounds (or until you feel a shift).

Decisions You Make

- You decide whether you want to tap on peace, or joy, or gratitude, or curiosity, or any other positive emotion.

- You decide whether to use both hands when tapping under each eye, under the collarbone, and on each side of the body.

- You decide how many fingers you use to tap; you may choose to use just your pointer finger, or just your pointer and middle fingers, or all your fingers.

- You can even vary how many fingers you use while tapping around, such as you might use just your pointer finger for the points on your face but then use all your fingers when tapping below your collarbone, on the side of your body, and on the top of your head.

Where to Tap

1. Use a finger on one hand to tap the outside edge of the other hand, or use the side of the pointer finger to do a karate chop motion against the outer edge of the other hand.

2. Tap at the start of your eyebrow (or eyebrows) near the bridge of your nose.

3. Tap at the outside of the eye (or both eyes).

4. Tap under the center of the eye (or both eyes).

5. Tap in the space below the nose and above the lips.

6. Tap below the lips, in the middle of the chin.

7. Tap below the center of the collarbone, inside the hollow part.

8. Tap on the side of the body (or on both sides) a few inches below the armpit.

9. Tap at the center of the top of the head.

FURTHER READING

The following reader-friendly books offer in-depth information and cited sources on topics introduced in this book.

Brown, Brené. *Atlas of the Heart: Mapping Meaningful Connection and Language of the Human Experience.* New York: Random House, 2021

Bryant, Thema. *Homecoming: Overcome Fear and Trauma to Reclaim Your Whole, Authentic Self.* New York: TarcherPerigee, 2022.

Burton, Robert A. *On Being Certain: Believing You Are Right Even When You're Not.* New York: St. Martin's Griffen, 2008.

Childre, Doc, Howard Martin, Deborah Rozman, and Rollin McCraty. *Heart Intelligence: Connecting with the Intuitive Guidance of the Heart.* Waterfront Digital Press, 2016.

Doidge, Norman. *The Brain That Changes Itself: Stories of Personal Triumph from the Frontiers of Brain Science.* New York: Penguin Books, 2015.

Duhigg, Charles. *The Power of Habit: Why We Do What We Do in Life and Business.* New York: Random House, 2012.

Goddard, Sally. *Reflexes, Learning, and Behavior: A Window into the Child's Mind.* Eugene, OR: Fern Ridge Press, 2002.

Graham, Linda. *Bouncing Back: Rewiring Your Brain for Maximum Resilience and Well-Being.* Novato, CA: New World Library, 2013.

Hanson, Rick. *Hardwiring Happiness: The New Brain Science of Contentment, Calm, and Confidence.* New York: Harmony Books, 2013.

Hawn, Goldie. *10 Mindful Minutes: Giving Our Children—and Ourselves—the Social and Emotional Skills to Reduce Stress and Anxiety for Healthy, Happier Lives.* New York: Perigee, 2011.

Kabat-Zinn, Jon. *Full Catastrophe Living: Using the Wisdom of Your Body and Mind to Face Stress, Pain, and Illness.* New York: Random House, 2009.

Kestly, Theresa A. *The Interpersonal Neurobiology of Play: Brain-Building Interventions for Emotional Well-Being.* New York: Norton, 2014.

Kolari, Jennifer. *Connected Parenting: Transform Your Challenging Child and Build Loving Bonds for Life.* New York: Avery, 2009.

Levine, Peter. *An Unspoken Voice: How the Body Releases Trauma and Restores Goodness.* Berkeley, CA: North Atlantic Books, 2010.

Lipton, Bruce H. *The Biology of Belief: Unleashing the Power of Consciousness, Matter, and Miracles.* Carlsbad, CA: Hay House, 2005.

McCraty, Rollin. *Science of the Heart: Exploring the Role of the Heart in Human Performance.* Vol. 2. Boulder Creek, CA: HeartMath Institute, 2015.

Porges, Stephen W. *The Pocket Guide to the Polyvagal Theory: The Transformative Power of Feeling Safe.* New York: Norton, 2017.

Sapolsky, Robert M. *Why Zebras Don't Get Ulcers: The Acclaimed Guide to Stress, Stress-Related Diseases, and Coping.* New York: St. Martin's Press, 2004.

Sharot, Tali. *The Influential Mind: What the Brain Reveals about Our Power to Change Others.* New York: Henry Holt, 2017.

Stanley, Elizabeth A. *Widen the Window: Training Your Brain and Body to Thrive During Stress and Recover from Trauma.* New York: Avery, 2019.

Stapleton, Peta. *The Science of Tapping: A Proven Stress Management Technique for the Mind and Body.* Carlsbad, CA: Hay House, 2019.

Van der Kolk, Bessel. *The Body Keeps the Score: Brain, Mind, and Body in the Healing of Trauma.* New York: Penguin Books, 2015.

ABOUT THE AUTHOR

For years, Nancy Sokol Green was a classroom teacher, teacher trainer, and author of innovative educational programs used in schools nationwide. In 1999, she created and implemented Brain Highways in the public schools, which has since evolved into an international program called Brain Highways Global.

She presently lives with her husband, along with her quirky, 75-pound golden retriever, and spends as much of her free time as possible with her nearby amazing daughters, sons-in-law, and grandkids.